WANDA HICKEY'S NIGHT OF GOLDEN
MEMORIES AND OTHER DISASTERS

Also by Jean Shepherd

IN GOD WE TRUST, ALL OTHERS PAY CASH
THE AMERICA OF GEORGE ADE

JEAN SHEPHERD

WANDA HICKEY'S NIGHT OF
Golden Memories
AND OTHER DISASTERS

Doubleday & Company, Inc., 1971, Garden City, New York

817.5
S

DRAWINGS BY RAYMOND DAVIDSON

These stories originally appeared in *Playboy* magazine. Copyright ©
1966, 1967, 1968, 1969, 1970 by HMH Publishing Co., Inc.

CONTENTS

To little Leigh with love. I hope it's been worth it all. . . .

WANDA HICKEY'S NIGHT OF GOLDEN MEMORIES AND OTHER DISASTERS

THE GRANDSTAND PASSION PLAY
OF DELBERT AND THE BUMPUS HOUNDS

" 'Mah-ree Elena, yore the answer to mah prayer. . . .' " The familiar twangy moan of old Gene Autry seemed to be coming from next to my ear. It was the first time I had ever dreamed in sound. Or *was* I dreaming?

"FER CHRISSAKE, WHAT THE HELL IS THAT RACKET?" The bedsprings clattered in the next room, as my old man cursed and leaped out of the sack, his feet thumping the floor in the dark. Instantly, I was wide awake.

" 'MAH-REE ELENA. . . .' " It was even louder, now that my mind was working again. The tinny plunking of a guitar cut through the darkness. My kid brother sat up in his bed across the room from me and began to whine, his usual reaction to any outside stimulus.

A guttural grunt of intense pain, followed by a high-pitched bleating wail, as the old man once again unerringly cracked his big toe against the leg of the dresser. He had done this so many times in the past, in

13

the dark, that all the varnish was now worn off the leg, and my father's toe was permanently shaped like a small tennis ball.

"Now what?" My mother joined in the chorus, her hair curlers rattling in the gloom.

"'WHEN IT'S TWAALAHT ON THE TRAY-ULL. . . .'" Autry had launched into another favorite of simpleminded millions everywhere.

"What the hell *time* is it?" muttered the old man. He was always an aggressive sleeper. Sleep was one of the things he did best, and he loved it. Some look upon sleep as an unfortunately necessary interruption of life; but there are others who hold that sleep *is* life, or at least one of the more fulfilling aspects of it, like eating or sex. Any time my old man's sleep was interrupted, he became truly dangerous.

"It's almost three-thirty. Who the hell's playing those goddamn records at three-thirty?"

Someone was, indeed, playing records at full blast. It was then that we first became aware of another sound— one that was to become more familiar and ominous in the weeks to come: a kind of snuffling, scratching, moiling, squealing, squishy turmoil.

"'. . . THAT SILVUHH HAI-UHD DAH-DEE OF MAHN. . . .'" Doors slammed. Twangy voices argued indistinctly. Gene Autry keened on and on. The snuffling squeals rose and fell. The old man reconnoitered silently through the bedroom curtains.

"HOOIICKK-PATOOOEY!" Something juicy splatted against the side of our house.

14

"Holy Christ!" The old man hissed a rhetorical comment to no one in particular.

"GRRAAAHHKKK! BROWWK!" A window-rattling burp boomed out over the scratchy Gene Autry disc.

My mother was finally galvanized into action. She had fought a lifelong battle against obscene noises of every variety. I could hear her pattering feet, as she joined my father at the window.

"Who *are* they?" she asked, after a pause to survey the scene.

"Damned if I know!" the old man answered; but I could tell from the sound of his voice that he knew trouble had arrived. Big trouble. The Bumpus crowd had moved in next door and was already in business.

Ours was not a genteel neighborhood, by any stretch of the imagination. Nestled picturesquely between the looming steel mills and the verminously aromatic oil refineries and encircled by a colorful conglomerate of city dumps and fetid rivers, our northern Indiana town was and is the very essence of the Midwestern industrial heartland of the nation. There was a standard barbershop bit of humor that said it with surprising poeticism: If Chicago (only a stone's throw away across the polluted lake waters) was Carl Sandburg's "City of the Broad Shoulders," then Hohman had to be that city's broad rear end.

According to legend, it bore the name of a hapless early settler who had arrived on the scene when the land was just prairie and Indian trails. Surveying the sparkling blue waters of Lake Michigan, he decided that

Chicago, then a tiny trading post where land was free for the asking, had no future. Struggling through the quagmires farther south, for some demented reason now lost to history, he set up camp and invested heavily in land that was destined to become one of the ugliest pieces of real estate this side of the craters of the moon. Indeed, it bore some resemblance to the moon, in that the natives were alternately seared by stifling heat in the summer and reduced to clanking hulks when the fierce gales blew off the lake. Our founding father set the pattern of futility for all future generations.

My old man, my mother, my kid brother and I slogged along in the great tradition. The old man had his high point every Wednesday at George's Bowling Alley, where he once rolled a historic game in which he got three consecutive strikes. My kid brother's nose ran steadily, winter and summer. My mother made red cabbage, peanut-butter-and-jelly sandwiches, meat loaf and Jell-O in an endless stream. And I studied the principal exports of Peru at the Warren G. Harding School.

Delbert Bumpus entered Warren G. Harding like a small, truculent rhinoceros. His hair grew low down on his almost nonexistent forehead, and he had the greatest pair of ears that Warren G. Harding had ever seen, extending at absolutely right angles from his head. Between those ears festered a pea-sized but malevolent brain that almost immediately made him the most feared kid below sixth grade.

He had a direct way of settling disagreements that he established on the second day of his brief but spectacu-

lar period at W.G.H. Grover Dill—our number-two-rank-
ing thug, right behind Scut Farkas, who stood alone
as the premier bully of all he surveyed—challenged
Bumpus to a showdown the first time he laid eyes on
those peculiarly provocative ears. It was recess time
and, as usual, we milled about aimlessly in the stickers
and sand hills of our playground. It was too early for
baseball; football had been over for months; we didn't
have a basketball hoop; so we just milled.

Spotting Bumpus in his worn blue jeans and black
turtleneck—tiny, close-set eyes almost invisible under a
thatch of jet-black, wiry hair—Dill opened negotiations,
his own slitted eyes glinting in anticipation of a little
action:

"What's yer name, kid?"

Bumpus pulled his head lower into the turtleneck and
said nothing.

"I SAID, WHAT'S YER NAME, KID?" This time in
a loud, trumpeting voice that alerted the rest of the
school ground that spring had come and Grover Dill
felt the sap rising. Bumpus, a full head and a half shorter
than Dill but built along the lines of a fireplug, muttered:

"Bumpus." It was the first word we had heard from
him, his accent redolent of the deepest Kentucky hills.

"BUMPUS! What the hell kind of a name is that? Holy
Moses! Didja hear that? Bumpus! What kind of a name
is that?"

Dill's humor, while extremely primitive, was refreshingly
direct. He began to sing in a high, feminine voice:

17

"Bumpus Schlumpus, double Crumpus—" He broke off, advancing on Bumpus, sandy hair abristle.

"D'ya have a first name, runt?"

Farkas watched with Olympian disinterest as his protégé moved in for the kill. Schwartz huddled next to me, ashen-faced, while Flick attempted to blend into the sand. There wasn't one of us who had not, at one time or another, been dealt with by either Farkas or Dill.

"I said, what's yer first name, kid?" Bumpus, backed up flat against the school wall, finally spoke up:

"Delbert."

"Delbert! *DELBERT!*" Outraged by such a name, Dill addressed the crowd, with scorn dripping from his every word. "*Delbert Bumpus!* They're letting *everybody* in Harding School these days! What the hell kind of a name is that? That must be some kind of *hillbilly* name!"

It was the last time anyone at Warren G. Harding ever said, or even thought, anything like that about Delbert Bumpus.

Everything happened so fast after that that no two accounts of it were the same. The way I saw it, Bumpus' head snapped down low between his shoulder blades. He bent over from the waist, charged over the sand like a wounded wart hog insane with fury, left his feet and butted his black, furry head like a battering-ram into Dill's rib cage, the sickening thump sounding exactly like a watermelon dropped from a second-story window. Dill, knocked backward by the charge, landed on his neck and slid for three or four feet, his face alternating green and white. His eyes, usually almost unseen behind

18

his cobra lids, popped out like a tromped-on toad-frog's. He lay flat, gazing paralyzed at the spring sky, one shoe wrenched off his foot by the impact. The schoolyard was hushed, except for the sound of a prolonged gurling and wheezing as Dill, now half his original size, lay retching. It was obvious that he was out of action for some time.

Bumpus glared around at the hushed faces, then spit a long stream of rich-brown tobacco juice onto Dill's left tennis shoe. The buzzer sounded for the end of recess, but it was the beginning of a new era.

That's the way the whole Bumpus crowd was, in one way or another. Overnight, the entire neighborhood changed. The Taylors, a quiet family who had lived next to us for years, had moved out and—without warning—the Bumpuses had flooded in. There were thousands of them! The house seemed to age in one week. What had been a nondescript bungalow became a battered, hinge-sprung, sagging hillbilly shack.

I remember only brief images of various Bumpuses. They never mixed with anyone else in the neighborhood, just moiled around, hawking, guffawing, kicking their dogs and piling up junk in the back yard. They drove an old slat-sided Chevy pickup truck that was covered with creamy-white bird droppings and a thick coating of rutted Kentucky clay. It had no windshield and the steering wheel looked like it was made entirely of old black friction tape. It roared like a tank, sending up clouds of blue smoke as it burned the sludge oil that the Bumpuses slopped into it. It seemed to be always hub-deep in mud, even though there was no mud in our neighborhood.

Old Emil Bumpus was kind of the headman. He was about eight feet tall and always walked like he was leaning into a strong wind, with his head hanging down around his overall tops. He must have weighed about 300 pounds, not including his chaw of navy plug, which he must have been born chewing. His neck was so red that at first we thought he always wore some kind of bandanna. But he didn't. He had an Adam's apple that rode up and down the front of his neck like a yo-yo. His hair, which was mud-colored, stuck out in all directions and looked like it had been chopped off here and there with a pair of hedge-trimming shears. And his hands, which hung down to just below his knees, had knuckles the size of pool balls, and there was usually a black, string bandage around a thumb. His hands were made for hitting things.

The Bumpuses weren't in town three days before Emil cleaned out the whole back room at the Blue Bird Tavern one night. They said somebody had given him a dirty look. Another time, Big Rusty Galambus, who had heard about that incident and felt his reputation was at stake, busted Emil's gallon jug over the back of his head. They said that Emil didn't even know he'd been hit for a couple of minutes, until somebody told him. Then he turned around, stood up, looked down at Big Rusty and said:

"Ah'd be mo' careful with that thar jug a mahn ef'n

ah was yew. Ef ah didn' know bettuh, ah mighta tho't yew was spoilin' for a fight."

There was something about the way he said it that persuaded Rusty, a scarred veteran of the open hearth, who had once hoisted the back end of a Ford truck with his bare hands when the jack busted, to apologize and say that the jug slipped.

Emil let it pass; after all, he had 9000 more jugs at home, of all sizes and shapes, sitting on various window sills. We wondered what they were for, until we saw the Bumpuses carrying in pieces of copper tubing—and until we got our first whiff of a mighty aroma from their basement that overpowered even the normal neighborhood smell from the Sinclair oil refinery a half mile away. It got so bad at times that starlings would sit around on the telephone wires back of the Bumpus house, just breathing deeply and falling off into the bushes and squawking. From time to time, there would be a dull explosion in the cellar, and a Bumpus would run out of the house with his overalls on fire.

One afternoon, with a snootful of whatever they were making down there, Emil came reeling out onto the back porch. He was yelling at somebody in the kitchen, his deep molasses drawl booming out over the neighborhood.

"WHO YEW THANK YO' TAWKIN' TEW?" With that, he grabbed ahold of the back porch and pulled it right off the house. He just grabbed the porch and yanked it out by the roots:

"AAAuuuggghhh!"

From that day on, the Bumpus house had no back porch, only a door about eight feet up in the air and a rusty screen. Once in a while, one of them would jump out—and land in the garbage. And every so often, one of the skinny, red-faced sisters would fall out accidentally, usually carrying a pail of dishwater or chicken innards.

"Lawd a'mighty. Amy Jo, ef'n yew cain't watch them clodhoppers a yourn, we gonna have to chain yew up!" Another raucous round of harrooping. They sure loved one another.

From the day they moved in, the house was surrounded by a thick swamp of junk: old truck tires, barrels full of bottles and tin cans, black oil drums, rusty pitchforks, busted chicken crates, an old bathtub, at least 57 ancient bedsprings, an old tractor hood, a half-dozen rotting bushel baskets overflowing with inner tubes and galoshes, a wheelbarrow with one handle, eight or nine horse collars and a lot of things that nobody could figure out—things that looked like big tall water boilers with pipes sticking out. For some reason, they loved wire; they had all kinds of it—chicken wire, baling wire and rolls of barbed wire, just sort of lying around. And in between the big stuff, there was all the little stuff: sardine cans, old batteries, tire irons, old blue tin cups, corncobs, leather straps and a lot of tire pumps. They were always bringing home license plates, which they nailed up by the basement door. The Bumpuses went to the city dump two or three times a week—like art patrons to a gallery—to stock up on more of the same.

The sea of wreckage spread like a blight onto the surrounding yards, first an ironing board on our lawn, then a bicycle tire in our bushes, then a few odd corncobs on the front porch. And one day, a gust of wind covered my mother's flapping laundry—her pride and joy—with a thin, indelible coating of chicken dung, pigeon feathers, rabbit fur and goat droppings. After that, her jaw was grim, her eyes thin slits of rage, every time another burst of hawkings or blattings reminded her of the Bumpuses. The night my old man tripped in the dark over a rusty radiator in our back yard, causing him to drop his bowling ball on his left foot, didn't help things, either. He grabbed the radiator and flung it into the dark, back into the Bumpuses' yard; it crashed into the rubble, and for five minutes, an avalanche of sound rumbled on and on, like Fibber McGee's closet. Emil stuck his head out of the kitchen window, quickly followed by the barrel of his trusty shotgun. When the old man stood his ground, Emil hissed, "Sic 'em, Luke!" Instantly, 17 dogs roared out from behind the garage. The old man barely made the kitchen.

A few days later, Schwartz, Kissel, Flick and I were trudging up our driveway when Flick stopped in his tracks, pointed and said, with a touch of delighted wonder, "Hey, look at that funny little house."

"Yeah, look at that little moon on it," replied Schwartz, likewise with some wonder.

"What the hell is it?" Junior Kissel chimed in.

Suddenly, Delbert Bumpus shot around the side of the house, dodging his way through the junk yard like a broken-field runner, and hurled himself headlong into the tiny pine shack and slammed the door, disappearing from our view—but not, unfortunately, beyond our earshot. It was then that we found out about little houses with moons, a new concept for all of us. Devout believers in eternal verities and ancient traditions, the Bumpuses obviously distrusted newfangled, citified contraptions such as that white-porcelain doohickey beside their upstairs bathtub, which didn't get much use, either—except, rumor had it, for the aging and storage of white lightning. From that day on, there was an endless stream of Bumpuses beating a path through the back yard at all hours of the day and night. The outhouse also solved for them the problem of what to do with last year's Sears, Roebuck catalog.

With the Bumpuses—and the outhouse—came the rats. They must have brought back a couple of thousand from one of their trips to the dump. Emil would squat out in back and pop at them with a long-barreled single-shot .22. You could hear the ricochets bouncing off the oil drums, and then Emil yelling:

"Gahdamn, Ima Pearl, ah missed that varmint agin."

"Emil, yew kin go out huntin' after supper. It's time we et."

The Bumpus hounds, who had their own problems with an even larger population of ticks and lice, had no interest at all in the rats. Once in a while, you'd see a hound sprawled flat on his back in the dust, legs spraddled, ears spread out, mouth hanging open, tongue lolling, sound asleep in the sun, with a rat lying beside him like they were the best of friends. The rats had no such nonaggression treaty with the Bumpus chickens, whom they ganged up on now and then, but their losses were too heavy to make it a regular thing. The Bumpuses had *mean* chickens. One big gray hen with a ratty tail and demented yellow eyes chased Schwartz all the way to school one day and waited in the playground for him to come out at recess. He wisely cowered in the locker room.

They also had rabbits—and pigeons. For some reason, hillbillies dearly love pigeons. They kept them in chicken-wire pens when they weren't out dive-bombing our yard and roosting on everybody's laundry. And the Bumpuses had one animal nobody could identify. It was kind of round, with blackish fur and claws. It weighed about 30 pounds or so, and Mrs. Kissel told my mother it was "a swamp bear." Nobody believed her, until one time it tried to eat Mrs. Gammie's Airedale, Rags, who had a nervous breakdown and had to be sent to the country. But the only atrocity it ever actually committed was to devour all my mother's iris bulbs. Emil used to holler at it once in a while, when it got to chewing on the truck tires. Its name was Jack.

The three goats never gave anybody much trouble; in fact, they kept our lawn mowed for us. They didn't smell too good if you got downwind of them on a warm day, but nobody complained about it—what with all the other indescribable smells that drifted our way day and night. My old man would peek out of the kitchen window with a Montgomery Ward spyglass to try to see what the Bumpuses ate when they were all squatting around the trough in the kitchen, with a yellow light bulb hanging overhead amid the wriggling flypaper. There was one smell that really used to get him. He could never tell what it was—a kind of smoky, greasy, gamy animal scent. Then one night he got it. He was watching them wolf it down, the way they always did, slurping and crunching, throwing off a thick yellow spray.

"By God, they're eating possum! That's what it is. Possum!"

My mother, who was always interested in cooking, asked: "Possum, what's that?"

A *Field & Stream* subscriber, the old man immediately answered, "Possum—you know, it's kind of a big rat." My mother, who was putting tomato paste on top of our meat loaf at the time, dropped her spoon and ran into the bathroom. After that, she didn't ask much about what the Bumpuses ate.

"I wonder where the hell they get it?" the old man continued. "I never heard of a possum around here." Where they got possum was just another of the Bumpus mysteries.

Every five minutes or so, someone threw something out the back window into the yard. My mother would be standing at the sink, peering out the window that looked right into the Bumpus house just across the driveway from us. A soggy paper sack filled with coffee grounds and apple cores would sail out and land amid the rubble.

"Tch, tch, just look at those pigs!"

She was right. We were living next door to a tightly knit band of total slobs, a genuine gypsy family. The Bumpuses were so low down on the evolutionary totem pole that they weren't even included in Darwin's famous family tree. They had inbred and ingrown and finally emerged from the Kentucky hills like some remnant of Attila the Hun's barbarian horde. Flick said that they had webbed feet and only three toes. It might have been true.

Delbert Bumpus, the runt of the litter, came to school about three days a month. It was three times too often. Whenever he showed up, there would be a lot of yelling, and they'd throw him out. Delbert never played with anybody and he hardly ever talked; but he spat a lot. Since he lived with the goats and rabbits and chickens, he didn't smell exactly like the rest of us, either—and *we* weren't any bargain.

One time, Miss Parsons, our gym teacher, made the mistake of putting Delbert in a volleyball game. I guess they never played volleyball in Kentucky, because at first he didn't seem to understand what was going on. But when he got the hang of it, everything changed. He stood there, watching them knock the ball back and forth, for maybe five minutes, and then somebody hit one toward him. He left the ground about three feet and gave the ball an overhand shot that sent it screaming over the net; it caught Schwartz just below the left eye and knocked him flat. Bumpus' side cheered.

Miss Parsons said, "No, Delbert, you mustn't hit it that hard."

Bumpus spat on the gym floor and glared at her for a minute, and then growled, "What the goddamn hell is this game 'spose ta be about?"

While Schwartz crawled around on the floor, crying, Miss Parsons—who taught Sunday school at the Baptist church—tried again.

"You mustn't use those bad words, Delbert. Now, let's begin the game again, shall we?"

Miss Parsons believed in law and order. Schwartz, who had been removed to the nurse's office, trailing blood, had been replaced by Roger Beanblossom, who, at the age of seven, was already six feet tall. Beanblossom, famous for his serve, sliced a whistler right at Bumpus, who stopped scratching just in time to slam the ball back over the net. This time, he got Jack Morton in the pit of his stomach, knocking the wind out of him like a deflated beach ball. He slumped to the floor, the color of Cream of Wheat.

"No, Delbert." Miss Parsons was back in the fray. "Here, I'll show you."

She tapped the ball delicately into the air, to show how the game was played. Bumpus, watching this exhibition, came out with a line that soon became legend at Warren G. Harding School.

"Who the hell wants to play a goddamn silly girl's game lahk that?"

Miss Parsons, now beet red and faced with a question many of us had privately asked, since volleyball was a hated game among the males of the school, could do only one thing. "Delbert Bumpus, you go to the office this instant!"

Picking his nose, Delbert slouched toward the door and muttered, with classic simplicity: "Screw you."

And he left. It was lucky that Miss Parsons didn't know what he meant by that, or there would have been real trouble. He was kicked out of school for only a week.

Then there was the time Miss Shields opened up the day by reading us a chapter of *Raggedy Ann and Raggedy Andy*. Miss Shields was tall and thin and wore rimless glasses. She was a very kind lady, who believed that all children were basically good.

"Boys and girls," she began, after setting the book down, "are there any questions?"

Bumpus, who had never asked a question, spoke up. He had a very deep voice for a kid; already it sounded a lot like old Emil's, rich and phlegmy.

"Yeah." That was all he said.

"Oh, you have a question, Delbert?" asked Miss Shields, obviously pleased. She felt at long last she was *reaching* him.

"Yeah." He was a kid of few words.

"Well, what is your question, Delbert?"

"Was this guy Raggedy Andy a bohunk?"

"What was that?" Miss Shields was caught off guard.

"Mah Uncle Cletus knew a bohunk onc't named Andy."

Miss Shields, who did not know Delbert Bumpus the way the class did, gamely replied: "Well, no, Delbert,

Raggedy Andy was not of Bohemian extraction. He was a doll."

"Well, ah'll be goddamned," he snorted.

"What was that, Delbert?" Miss Shields felt the class slipping from her grasp.

"You mean a doll that walked aroun'? Shee-it!"

"Delbert, you mustn't use words like that in class. Yes, Raggedy Andy was a doll who walked around, and so was Raggedy Ann."

Delbert snorted again in disbelief and, as he sat down, said in a loud voice, "Ah nevah did heah such a crock a hog drippin's."

"Delbert," said Miss Shields with an ashen face, "report to the office this instant!" We waited for him to say what he usually said when he left the room, but I guess he liked Miss Shields. He just stalked out and went home.

The only time Delbert ever said anything to me directly was one day when I made the mistake of throwing him out at first base. He looked at me real hard for a long time and then said: "Doan' worry, piss-ant, ah'll git yew someday."

Little did I dream at the time what form his revenge would take.

Delbert was the only Bumpus kid in my grade, but they infested Warren G. Harding like termites in an outhouse. There was Ima Jean, short and muscular, who was in the sixth grade, when she showed up, but spent most of her time hanging around the poolroom. There was a lanky, blue-jowled customer they called Jamie, who ran the still and was the only one who ever wore shoes. He and his brother Ace, who wore a brown fedora and blue work shirts, sat on the front steps at home on the Fourth of July, sucking at a jug and pretending to light sticks of dynamite with their cigars when little old ladies walked by. There were also several red-faced girls who spent most of their time dumping dishwater out of windows. Babies of various sizes and sexes crawled about the back yard, fraternizing indiscriminately with the livestock. They all wore limp, battleship-gray T-shirts and nothing else. They cried day and night.

We thought that was all of them—until one day a truck stopped in front of the house and out stepped a girl who made Daisy Mae look like Little Orphan Annie. My father was sprinkling the lawn at the time; he wound up watering the windows. Ace and Emil came running out onto the porch, whooping and hollering. The girl carried a cardboard suitcase—in which she must have kept all her underwear, if she owned any—and wore her blonde hair piled high on her head; it gleamed in the midday sun. Her short muslin dress strained and bulged. The truck roared off. Ace rushed out to greet her, bellowing over his shoulder as he ran:

"MAH GAWD! HEY, MAW, IT'S CASSIE! SHE'S HOME FROM THE REFORMATORY!"

Emil grabbed her suitcase and Cassie, the ripest 16-year-old ever to descend on northern Indiana, kissed her father in a way that clouded up windows for blocks around.

"Mah Gawd, Cassie, yew sure filled out!" he boomed,

31

slapping her none too paternally on the backside. Maw Bumpus, drying her hands on her apron, yelled from the porch:

"YEW GIT IN HERE, CASSIE, AN' LEAVE YORE PAW ALONE. LEASTWAYS TILL WE'VE ET."

After that, my father stepped up his spyglass work considerably, since they had no window shades and Cassie liked to dress very casually around the house. She also liked to lie in the swing on the front porch and suck jawbreakers when the weather was hot.

On Saturday nights, even before Cassie arrived, a roaring fleet of old cars would park around the Bumpus house and a mob of slope-browed, slack-jawed friends and relatives would crowd into the place. All night, paneless windows needlessly flung wide, a thunderous square dance would shake the crockery for blocks around. Hawking and spitting and swilling applejack, they yelled and sweated and thumped up and down, while old Emil sat in a corner and sawed on his fiddle. On those nights, hardly anyone dared leave their homes. These parties always ended one way—with a sudden crash, a prolonged scuffle and then:

"EF'N YEW LAY ANOTHA FINGA ON MAH WOMAN, AH'LL SLICE YEW UP LIKE HOG BACON!"

"YEW AN' WHO ELSE, YEW SONOVABITCH!?"

Followed by screams, crashing bottles, running feet; then a distant wail of sirens. A tremendous roaring of ancient motors, a cloud of gravel and they were all gone, leaving a trail of blood and sweat behind them.

32

Then there were the dogs. They had at least 745 dogs. Now, our neighborhood had always had dogs—walking-around, ordinary dogs, with names like Zero and Ralph. Once in a while, one of them would knock over a garbage can, but they were dogs that knew their place. The Bumpus hounds, on the other hand, didn't seem to be dogs at all, or maybe they were such *total* dogs that no one knew how to handle them. They were the most uninhibited animals you ever saw in your life. They had absolutely no sense of privacy. They did everything in the bright sunlight, and I mean *everything*. They were just a great churning mass of tails and tongues and flea-bitten bodies. You could almost see the smell. On a warm day, a sort of bluish-greenish-yellowish haze hung over the Bumpus house, and even the haze had fleas.

Every day, one of the Bumpus women would swing down from the back door to feed them. She strode amid the slavering pack, carrying a greasy dishpan full of obscene table scraps and chicken gizzards.

"COME AN' GIT YO' VITTLES!"

The mob would charge, rolling over her in a tidal wave of heaving flanks, bloodshot eyes and mangy fur. Snarling and squealing, they stormed over the littered back yard, a heaving ball of yapping curs. The Bumpus woman, fastidiously shifting her wad of tobacco from one side of her mouth to the other, would then kick her way through the pack and back into the house.

They dug holes continously—under the porch, in the back yard, in the middle of our scrawny lawn and under the car. Five of them took up residence beneath our garage. They slept there in shifts 24 hours a day. Every time the old man would drive the Olds in, we'd hear under the floor: "ROWFF OUFFF ROWWFF!" and they'd run in mad circles around the garage.

"Shoo! Beat it! Lemme alone!" my father would shout, as he hopped up and down amid the hounds, fighting his way toward the kitchen door. We'd see the eyes of the Bumpus family peering out, waiting for him to make a wrong move. They were a real hillbilly family when it came to their dogs. You could say anything you wanted about anybody in the family, but you didn't dare insult one of their dogs. You didn't say anything against Old Blue or Big Red. *All* the dogs—with the exception of those 17 named Luke—were named either Big Red or Old Blue.

Half a dozen times a week, my old man would come sprinting up the back steps just a stride ahead of the leader of the pack—a wiry, scarred battler named, of course, Big Red—baying the way Kentucky hounds always do when they've got a bear up a tree. Every time this would happen, there would be another wave of juicy guffaws and wheezy backslapping from the Bumpus mob. This really burned the old man up. After a hard day at the office and the Olds' acting up again, fighting off Big Red to get into the kitchen really got him. He'd sit at the kitchen table, his face sweaty, gulping down a bottle of Atlas Praeger. Finally, after catching his breath, he'd say, "Goddamn it, did you see what those lousy hounds did to the hedge?"

My mother, who had long since given up caring, al-

34

ways shrugged her shoulders and continued stoically scouring her pots.

When there was a full moon, the Bumpus hounds, feeling some ancient canine urge, would treat the neighborhood to a nightlong serenade.

"OwwwwwOOOOOOOOOOOOOOOO. WOWOOOOO-OOOOOooooooooo. Yap yap yaoooOOOOOOooooooooo-oo."

One after the other, they would take solos; then, after a blessed moment of silence, a full chorus, 15 or 20 strong, would howl to the inconstant moon:

"Yipe yipe yaaWOOOOOOOOooooooooo. Ow Ow OW-OOOOOOO. OOOOOOOooooooWOWOOO WOW! WOW! WOWOOOoooooo."

All over the neighborhood, in darkened bedrooms, hairs rose on reddened necks, children whimpered in fear. The Bumpus hounds bayed on, interspersed with Gene Autry—"MEXICALI ROSE, KEEP SMILIN', AH'LL COME BACK TO YEW . . .'"—and the running commentary of the Bumpuses themselves: "HOICK-PA-TOOEY."

Months went by. We were in a state of siege. Only after you've lived next to a family like the Bumpuses can you understand how anyone could carry on a lifelong feud with his neighbors. My mother and father were just standard-type people. The old man would flip his cork once in a while when the furnace went on the fritz; he'd threaten to blow out his brains when the White Sox traded away the only ballplayer they had. But he never got mad enough to throw rocks at people—not until that fantastic day when the rumbling volcano of his temper, roused from dormancy by the arrival of the Bumpuses, finally erupted.

Every three of four months—roughly three times a year—we would make a major food investment. I suppose rich families don't even think about this kind of thing, but ordinary families in those days spent their lives eating canned corn, meat loaf, peanut-butter sandwiches, oatmeal, red cabbage and peas. In such a home, the great meals that came along every few months stuck out like icebergs in the Caribbean. Buying a turkey was a state occasion. The entire family would go to the market to inspect all the turkeys; they'd discuss the relative merits of each, press the breastbones down, wiggle the legs, until finally they'd take a vote and decide on this particular 12-pounder, which is borne home with honor and prepared for the big day, like a virgin for the sacrifice. It's a ritual almost as cherished and time-honored as the moment when the tribe hunkers around the ceremonial campfire to devour it.

For weeks afterward, the theological debates continue:

"That was a very good turkey. Very good."

"It was almost as good as the turkey we had in Thirty-three."

"But it wasn't quite as tender as the one we had in Twenty-nine. Actually, this year's was a little dry."

These feast days are always associated with major holidays: turkey for Thanksgiving and Christmas, roast chicken for birthdays and, in our house, Easter always meant ham. My father was totally ape over ham. The

36

week before Easter, usually on Friday night, he'd say, "I'll tell you what let's do. What do you say we all pile in the car, drive down to the A.&P. and pick out a great big ham for Easter?"

He said it almost nonchalantly, but his eyes would be lit with a wild and ravenous light. It was no small thing he was suggesting, since "a great big ham" meant about half his pay check in those days.

My mother almost always would come back with, "Well, gee, I don't know. Can we afford it this year? We can always get a nice little pot roast."

"Ah, come on! What the hell. You only live once. What do you say?" And she would always relent.

Quivering slightly, he would throw on his coat and rush to the door. He could already see the ham half eaten, rich and red, weeks of magnificent pickings. Nothing goes with Atlas Praeger like cold ham after a session at the bowling alley.

We'd race to the A. & P. All the hams would be laid out, wrapped in white paper, some marked Armour Star, others Swift; not to mention Hormel. There were always great arguments as to which was really best. These were not dinky little canned hams but weighty monsters smoked darkly and tied with greasy, twisted twine.

The old man would go up and down the case, poking, peering, hefting, sniffing, occasionally punching, until, eventually, *the* ham was isolated from the common herd. Somehow, it looked a little different from the rest. It was *our* ham.

We would leave the market with at least four giant

bags of groceries, our fare for the week: loaves of Wonder Bread, Campbell's tomato soup, Ann Page pork and beans, eggs, a two-pound jar of grape jelly, fig bars, oatmeal, Cream of Wheat—real *people* food—and the ham. *The* ham.

When we got the ham home, my mother immediately stripped off the white paper and the string in the middle of our chipped white-enamel kitchen table. There it lay, exuding heavenly perfumes—proud, arrogant, regal. It had a dark, smoked, leathery skin, which my mother carefully peeled off with her sharpened bread knife. Then the old man, the only one who could lift the ham without straining a gut, placed it in the big dark-blue oval pot that was used only for hams. My mother then covered the ham with water, pushed it onto the big burner and turned up the gas until it boiled. It just sat there on the stove and bubbled away for maybe two hours, filling the house with a smell that was so luscious, so powerful as to have erotic overtones. The old man paced back and forth, occasionally lifting the lid and prodding the ham with a fork, inhaling deeply. The ham frenzy was upon him.

After about an hour, the whole neighborhood knew what we were having for Easter. Finally, the next phase began. Grunting and straining, my mother poured off the water into another pot. It would later form the base of a magnificent pea soup so pungent as to bring tears to the eyes. She then sprinkled a thick layer of brown sugar, dotted with butter, over the ham. She stuck cloves in it in a crisscross design, then added several slices of

Del Monte pineapple, thick and juicy, and topped it off with a maraschino cherry in the center of each slice. She then sprinkled more brown sugar over the lot, a few teaspoons of molasses, the juice from the pineapple can, a little salt, a little pepper, and it was shoved into the oven. Almost instantly, the brown sugar melted over the mighty ham and mingled with the ham juice in the pan.

By this time, the old man, humming nervously to himself, had checked his carving set several times, to make sure the knife was honed, the fork tines sharp—while in the oven, the ham baked on and on, until late Saturday night, when my mother finally turned off the gas, leaving the oven unopened and the ham inside. She said, as she always did, "Never eat a baked ham right after it's baked. Let it sit in the oven for twelve hours at least."

All night long, I would lie in my bed and smell the ham. The next day was Easter: Easter eggs and chocolate bunnies and all that. But the ham and only the ham was what really counted—not only for itself but because it always put my father in a great mood. We would play catch tomorrow; he would drink beer and tell stories. For once, the Bumpuses would be forgotten. Who the hell cares about a bunch of hillbillies, when there's baked him on the table? I lay in my bed, awake, the dark, indescribable aroma of ham coiling sinuously into my bedroom from the kitchen. In the next room, my father snored lustily, resting up for the great feast.

Immediately after breakfast the next morning, while my brother and I crawled around the house, looking for Easter eggs, my mother turned on the oven to heat the ham ever so slowly. This is important, she told us. The flame must be very low.

By 1:30 that afternoon, the tension had risen almost to the breaking point. The smell of ham saturated the drapes. And on my trip down to Pulaski's for the Sunday paper, I found that it could be smelled at least four blocks away. Finally, at about two o'clock, we all gathered around while my mother opened the blue pot—releasing a blast of fragrance so overwhelming that my knees wobbled—and surrounded the ham with sliced sweet potatoes to bake in the brown sugar and pineapple juice.

We usually had our Easter meal around three. Everything was timed carefully around the ham and the Parker House rolls. About 30 minutes before H hour, my mother took the ham out of the oven and laid it out on a big sheet of wax paper, right in the middle of the kitchen table, to let it cool a bit and set—the thick, sweet, brown molasses and sugar oozing down over the sides, the pineapple slices baked brown, the cloves like tiny black insects soaking in the hot ham gravy.

Easter that year was the way all Easters should be but rarely are. Spring had come early, for a change. There were years when winter's hard rock ice was still visible along the curbs, blackened and filthy, coated with steel-mill grime, until late in May. But this Easter was different; gentle breezes blew through the kitchen screen door. Already the stickers in our yard gave promise of a bumper crop. The air was balmy and heavy with spring passion about to burst.

The spring sunlight slanted in through the kitchen window and bathed the ham in a golden, suffused light, just like any good religious experience should be lit. The old man was in an exalted state of anticipation. Whenever he really got excited, he would crack his knuckles loudly. On this fateful day, he was popping them like a set of Brazilian castanets. He had on the new white shirt that he had gotten the week before at J. C. Penney.

While the ham sat basking in our gaze, my mother busily spread the lace tablecloth on the dining-room table and set out our best china, which was used only three or four times a year at the maximum. My father picked up his carving knife again, for one last stroke on the whetstone. He held the blade up to the light. Everything was ready. He went into the living room and sat down.

"Ah."

His eyes glowed with the primal lust of a cave man about to dig into the kill, which would last us at least four months. We would have ham sandwiches, ham salad, ham gravy, ham hash—and, finally, about ten gallons of pea soup made with the gigantic ham bone.

When it happened, he was sitting knee-deep in the *Chicago Tribune* sports section. I had been called in to wash up. My mother was in the bedroom, removing the curlers from her hair. My Aunt Glenn and Uncle Tom were on their way over to have Easter dinner with us. Uncle Tom always gave me a dollar. It was going to be a day to remember. Little did I suspect why.

I had just left the bathroom and my kid brother had just gone in for his fumigation, when suddenly and without warning:

BLAM!

The kitchen door flew open. It had been left ajar just a crack to let the air come in to cool the ham.

I rushed to the kitchen just in time to see 4293 blue-ticked Bumpus hounds roar through the screen door in a great, roiling mob. The leader of the pack—the one that almost got the old man every day—leaped high onto the table and grabbed the butt end of the ham in his enormous slavering jaws.

The rest of the hounds—squealing, yapping, panting, rolling over one another in a frenzy of madness—pounded out the kitchen door after Big Red, trailing brown sugar and pineapple slices behind him. They were in and out in less than five seconds. The screen door hung on one hinge, its screen ripped and torn and dripping with gravy. Out they went. Pow, just like that.

"HOLY CHRIST!" The old man leaped out of his chair. "THE HAM! THE HAM! THOSE GODDAMN DOGS! THE HAM!!"

He fell heavily over the footrest as he struggled to get into the kitchen, his voice a high-pitched scream of disbelief and rage. My mother just stood in the dining room, her face blank and staring, two aluminum hair curlers still in place. I ran through the kitchen, following my old man out to the back porch.

The snarling mob had rolled across the back yard and was now battling it out next to the garage, yipping and

42

squealing with excitement. Occasionally, one of them would be hurled out of the pack, flipping over backward in the air, to land heavily amid the barrel staves and sardine cans. Instantly, he would be back in the fray, biting and tearing at whatever moved.

The ham didn't last eight seconds. Old Grandpa Bumpus and a dozen other Bumpuses stuck their heads out of various windows, to see what all the yowling was about. Without pausing to aim, he reared back and spit a great big gob of tobacco juice—a new long-distance record—right into the middle of the pack. It was a direct hit on our ham—or what was left of it.

He whooped wildly, wattles reddening with joy, spraying tobacco juice in all directions, while Cletus, his dim-witted grandson, yelled from the basement door:

"GAHDAMN, GRAN'PAW, LOOKA THEM HOUN'S GO! LOOKA THEM OL' BOYS GO! HOT DAMN!!"

Delbert, meanwhile, circled around the roaring inferno, urging them on, kicking dogs that had given up back into the fray. Suddenly, he looked up at where I was hiding, a sadistic grin on his face, his hair hanging low. Our eyes met significantly for a fleeting instant and then he went back to kicking. A paralyzing fear gripped me. I remembered! That time I threw him out at first! Was this what he meant? Was *I* responsible for this tragedy? Oh, God, no! I slunk back into the shadows.

Bumpus women, their lank hair streaming down over their red necks, cackled fiendishly. Emil Bumpus, who had been asleep under the front porch, came reeling out, trailing his jug of white lightning. He took one look and practically passed out, wheezing and harrumphing and gurgling with hilarity.

My old man just stood stock-still on the back porch for a long moment, and then he blew his stack. I had never seen him do anything before that came near what he did now. We kept bottles on the back porch to be returned to the grocery store. He reached down and grabbed a milk bottle. His face white with rage, he wound up mightily and, with a sweeping, sidearm motion, hurled the bottle against the side of the Bumpus house with a deafening crash.

Grandpa Bumpus stopped in mid-spit, a big juicy gob hanging down over his chin. Emil dropped his jug to the ground, eyes lighting up with joy. This was back home for Emil. He was in his element. Turning around as if to run for his shotgun, he paused when he saw the old man standing there unmoving—radiating the clearest and most beautiful rage I'd ever seen in my life.

I cowered next to the railing on the back porch. Even the dogs felt his hatred. One by one, they fell silent. The bare, shiny bone of the ham lay in the sun. Big Red licked his chops.

After a long, pregnant moment, the old man turned, walked back into the kitchen and slammed the door. He stood for a minute by the kitchen table, looking down at the big sheet of wax paper dripping warm ham gravy. The heavenly aroma still hung heavy in the house. The old man just stood there—and came as close to crying as I'd ever seen him come.

Finally, he spoke, in a low, rasping voice: "All right!

OK! Get your coats. We're going to the Chinese joint. We're going to have chop suey."

Ordinarily, this would have been a gala of the highest order, going to the chop-suey joint. Today, it had all the gaiety of a funeral procession. The meal was eaten completely in silence.

That was the beginning of the bitter Shepherd-Bumpus feud. Relentlessly, the old man beleaguered the Bumpuses at every moment. He had tap-dancing cleats put on his shoes, which proved to be quite a nasty surprise to Big Red the first day he tried his usual ankle grab and caught a cleat behind his left ear. The old man took up tobacco chewing and arched long, undulating gobs onto the Bumpuses front porch when the wind was right. Every time the Bumpuses cranked up for a Gene Autry record festival, the old man countered with *In a Persian Market* played at full blast on our Sears, Roebuck Silvertone phonograph.

He took to throwing beer bottles out of the kitchen window and hurling coffee grounds onto the roof of the Bumpus truck when it bellowed by, taking the Bumpuses down to pick up their weekly relief check. He put bottle caps and tacks in the driveway and laughed uproariously every time one of the Bumpus women fell out the back door. He planted stickers in the cave that the Bumpus hounds lived in under the garage and took to jumping up and down on the garage floor late at night, when the hounds were asleep. Once he even bayed at the moon louder than all the hounds put together. I still remember the startled look on Big Red's face when the old man let out a long, drawn-out, quavering howl that he had learned from 20 years of watching Tarzan pictures.

The only trouble was that nothing he did—but *nothing*—made the slightest dent on the Bumpus way of life. They didn't even seem to know he was doing anything. The bottle caps and tacks he threw in the driveway never even scratched their feet, horny-hard after generations of shoelessness. The only thing that came of it was that we got two flats in one day on the Olds. His pitiful tobacco juice added as much to the sea that the Bumpuses themselves produced as a raindrop in the ocean. Nothing he could do had any effect. One night, he told my mother he had concluded that the Bumpuses *planned* the ham raid, the dogs carrying out their orders like guerrilla fighters. He hinted that he had something up his sleeve that he was working out in the basement that would really settle the score once and for all. He was biding his time.

The Bumpuses, meanwhile, went on with life as usual. There wasn't much they could do to us that they hadn't already done without intending to. Grandpa Bumpus jacked up his output of tobacco juice a little, but the rest of them just went about their business—collecting junk and piling it in the yard, tossing potato peels out the window, brewing moonshine, hollering, hitting each other and scratching themselves.

Then one night, without warning, everything changed forever. I awoke suddenly about three A.M. with a strange feeling that something was wrong. It was. For a couple of minutes, I couldn't focus my mind; then, gradually, it became clear to me that something was up. I heard my father in the next room. He had apparently awakened about the time I had.

He said hoarsely to my mother, "Hey, wake up!"

Then a long period of silence, while he listened in the darkness. We were always having alarums and excursions, but this was really different.

The bedsprings squeaked and the old man's feet pattered across the bedroom floor; the usual thump and groan of excruciating pain as he stubbed the foot of the dresser. A rustling silence as he peered through the curtains into the blackness of the night.

"Shhhhh!"

Another pause. I waited, scared and anxious in my bed, my kid brother mewing softly across the room.

"I'll be damned!" the old man said aloud in wonder. "You'll never believe it."

"Believe what?" whispered my mother, who had gotten up and joined him.

"Just take a look out there," he said with disbelief. "They moved out! They're gone!"

I realized why I had awakened. For the first time in many months, the sound of Gene Autry records had ceased; the continuous whine and yelp of the Bumpus hounds had been silenced. Everything was—*quiet*.

My father sniffed noisily.

"The smell is gone. Even the smell is gone!"

It was true. The air in my bedroom was clear of cabbage, dog urine and corn whiskey for the first time in six months.

The next morning, the truth was there for all to see. The Bumpuses had packed up and moved on, leaving behind a sagging shambles of a house, the back yard rutted and ground to gray dust by the endless clawings and scratchings of the Bumpus dogs and the Bumpus chickens, with great, tangled rat's nests of rusting junk and weather-beaten barrels, and smelly gallon jugs and empty bean cans that told everything there was to know about the way the Bumpuses lived out their days. They just ran up a big enough rent bill and then moved out in the middle of the night. We never heard another word about them.

At first, my father seemed to be glad. Then, about a month later, a nice old couple moved in next door and soon had the house and yard looking like an illustration for an insurance company that sold retirement plans to nice old couples. They went to bed every night at 8:30 and had a canary as a pet.

One night at supper, after a couple of beers, the old man finally said it:

"You know, they cleaned out just when I was going to hand 'em my crusher. I'll bet they did it on purpose." He got kind of moody for a while after that. We never found out what he had planned.

I struggled frantically to my feet, spilling Diet Pepsi over the front of my brocade smoking jacket as I flailed about. There wasn't a second to lose. Lurching forward, grasping for the knob, I fell heavily over the coffee table. On hands and knees, I scrambled forward, hoping to kill the TV set before it was too late. With a groan, I realized that once again, I had lost. The late-late-movie curse had struck again. I sat back to accept my fate.

I was trapped by one of the worst ever, a bucolic horror that I had taken care to avoid, when it was first released, by walking on the opposite side of the street from any moviehouse that played it. In a sky-blue suit and straw skimmer, Dick Haymes stood framed against the movie version of the Indiana countryside, dotted with quaint corn shocks and tinted with lurid oranges and greens, at the entrance to an archetypal Hollywood state fair. A few minutes later, there was the mandatory Old Gramps perched atop a sulky in the big trotting race, and The

51

Girl, rosy-cheeked and beribboned, who watched walleyed while Dick soulfully serenaded the Indiana moon.

Vainly I watched for a single glimpse of the Indiana fairs I had known—the Indiana fairs nobody makes movies about—but it never came. As Haymes warbled on, his eyes twinkling with boyish sincerity, my own grainy movie of a real Indiana fair began to unwind in memory.

As the scene opens, Schwartz, Flick, Junior Kissel and I are standing around back of the Sherwin-Williams paint sign in a misty drizzle. We are discussing current events, as was our wont. Schwartz had found half a can of Copenhagen snuff in the weeds, which we had all tried. After sneezing and gagging violently for 15 minutes, we took up our conversation where it had been interrupted by Schwartz' discovery. The dialog begins:

"My old man says if you ride on the whip too often, it scrambles your brains and you can't think good anymore," said Flick, whose nose was running copiously as a result of the snuff. "And it stunts your growth."

"That must have been what happened to *you*, Kissel," said Schwartz, spitting out a shred of snuff between his teeth. "That's why you're such a shrimp. You musta rode that thing fifty times last year."

Kissel, a full half head shorter than any of us, said nothing at this, realizing that it was the truth.

"Well, I don't care what your old man says, Flick," I said. "I'm gonna ride on the whip—and the caterpillar, too. There are so many things that stunt your growth and make you crazy, you might as well do it that way as any other." My wisdom, as usual was profound.

The rain drizzled down steadily, carrying with it its full load of blast-furnace dust and other by-products of the steel mills and oil refineries that ringed the town like iron dinosaurs. We wandered down the alley, kicking Carnation milk cans into imaginary goals as our conversation dragged on.

"One thing I'm gonna get is one of them red taffy apples!" Kissel shouted as he rooted around in somebody's garbage, looking for another can to kick.

"My old man says they stunt your growth, too. That red stuff clamps your teeth together so you can't grow good," said Schwartz as he pretended to sink an imaginary basket against a sagging backboard hanging on one of the garages that lined the alley.

"Yeah, well, your old man should know. He's about three feet tall," Kissel lashed back, cackling fiendishly, as Schwartz threw a half-eaten potato in his direction.

The next scene is a couple of hours later. My old man, my mother, my kid brother, Randy, and I are sitting around the kitchen table eating meat loaf, mashed potatoes and red cabbage. The old man takes a swallow of his beer and says, "It doesn't make any difference to me if you want to look at the quilts and raspberry preserves, as long as we get to see the first heat."

"Then Randy and I'll meet you two after the races," said my mother as she got up to put the coffee on. My kid brother immediately began to whimper piteously.

"You can have a taffy apple," she said to him from the stove. He stopped sobbing.

"One of those red ones?" he sniffed.

"Any color you want."

That was enough for him.

"Well, kid. . . ." The old man batted my arm.

"We'll watch Iron Man Gabruzzi give 'em hell to-morrow." As far as he was concerned, county fairs *were* dirt-track races. All that farm stuff was for the birds.

I went to bed happy. My brother and I whispered back and forth about the great stuff that would happen the next day. He was a Ferris-wheel nut who would have been glad to spend his whole life going around and around on a big wheel that creaked. Come to think of it, that's as good a way to spend it as any.

"I'll get that son of a bitch yet!" my old man's voice hissed suddenly and venomously through the darkened house.

Gawhang! Whap! Gawhang! Whap! Gawhang! Whap-whap!

My parents' bed squeaked dangerously as he leaped up and down on it, batting away at his old enemy. Every night in the late summer and early autumn, mosquito squadrons flew miles from the swamp to seek him out. The minute the lights were off, they dove to the attack. Flying in tight formations, they strafed again and again. The old man loved every minute of it. Fighting mosquitoes was his favorite sport. He slept with his personal fly swatter always at his side; he also had a loaded flit-gun, but he preferred the swatter. It was more sporting, somehow.

Whap! Whap! Bang! Something crashed in the darkness.

54

"Got the bastard!" He laughed exultantly. The battle was over—until the next hot puff of air brought in reinforcements. Our screens served only to keep the more enormous mosquitoes out of the house, allowing the smaller, lither, angrier types free access. During the second lull between attacks, I drifted off to sleep.

ZZZZZZRRRRIIIIINNNNGGGGGG!

The alarm clock blasted me hysterically into consciousness. Gray Saturday-morning light filled the house. The old man cursed and muttered sleepily as my mother padded out into the kitchen in her bathrobe and curlers to get the scrambled eggs started.

An hour later, we were in the Pontiac on the way to the county fair. The ill-fated Pontiac was an inexplicable interruption of the old man's lifelong devotion to the Oldsmobile. He was an Oldsmobile man the way others were Baptists, Methodists, Catholics or Holy Rollers. He later recanted after this episode of backsliding and returned to the fold with the purchase of a 1942 Oldsmobile station wagon that appealed far more deeply to his flamboyantly masochistic nature. A block or so ahead of us, Ludlow Kissel's battered Nash, loaded with kids and Mrs. Kissel (who weighed 360 pounds and read *True Romance*), struggled toward the fairgrounds. His Nash laid down a steady cloud of blue-white exhaust that hung over Cleveland Street like a destroyer's smoke screen. Junior Kissel peered out of the grimy back window, grinning wildly.

"Old Lud is sober. That makes the second time this summer," said my father as he struggled with the Pontiac, which had started shimmying again. It had bad king-pins.

Ten minutes later, we were out on Route 41, bumper to bumper in the great tangle of cars all headed for the fair. The sun rose higher over the distant steel mills. Steadily, the temperature and humidity rose until the sky was one vast copper sheet. We inched along like an endless procession of ants across a sizzling grill.

In the front seat, my mother fanned herself with a paper fan marked ORVILLE KLEEBER COAL AND ICE—REASONABLE. The flat fan was cut in the shape of a lump of coal. It had a wooden handle. She always kept it in the car for days like this.

"WHAT THE HELL YOU DOING, JERK?" barked the old man, head stuck aggressively out the window, at the driver ahead of us. His neck was red from sweat; his pongee shirt clung limply to his wiry frame; and his drugstore sunglasses dripped sweat as he glared through the heat waves and exhaust fumes at the idiot ahead.

"SLEEPING JESUS, YOU GONNA PARK THAT WRECK OR DRIVE IT?"

"Little pitchers have big ears," my mother intoned automatically, gazing placidly out her window at a Burma-Shave sign. The old man's latest curse—one of an endless lexicon—was a new one to me. I filed it away for future use. It might come in handy during a ball game or an argument with Schwartz.

It was now well past noon, but we were getting close. Far ahead, we could see the enormous, billowing cloud of dust that rose from the fairgrounds. Excitement mounted in the Pontiac as we shimmied closer and closer to the scene of action. Suddenly, with a great hissing, scalding roar, the radiator of the car ahead boiled over. Drops of red, rusty sludge streaked down over our windshield and spattered on the hood.

"OH, NO! FER CHRISSAKE, NO!"

The old man pounded on the steering wheel in rage as the lumbering Buick wheezed to a halt. The driver, a beet-faced man wearing a stiff blue-serge suit and a Panama hat, stumbled out of the car and raised the hood. A white cloud of steam enveloped him from head to toe.

"Goddamn it! There goes the first heat. Son of a bitch! Gimme a bottle of pop."

Silently, my mother opened a bottle of Nehi orange and handed it to him. She passed one back to me and gave my kid brother another. I felt the stinging carbonation sizzle through my nostrils as I guzzled the luke-warm contents.

Ahead, the other occupants of the Buick had gathered around the car and were fanning the hood with somebody's white shirt. The steam rose higher into the heavens. The car behind us began honking; then others joined in. This only bugged the old man even more. Out the window went his head.

"SHUT UP, YOU JERKS!" he yelled at the line of cars. They honked even louder.

The Buick was not the only car giving off steam. Several others had begun to percolate in the heat around us. The crowd ahead had begun to push the Buick off the road, like some great wounded whale. There is nothing deader than a dead Buick.

Finally, we were able to squeeze past the stragglers and once again move on toward the fairgrounds. A biplane towing a red-and-white streamer droned over the line of traffic: FISH DINNER ALL YOU CAN EAT $1.69 JOE'S DINER RTE. 6.

We were so close now that the sounds of the fair began to drift in over the roar of motors: calliopes bleating, whistles, merry-go-round music, bells ringing, barkers. Two cops in short-sleeved blue shirts waved the cars in through the main gate and past a cornfield to the jam-packed, rutted parking lot just inside the grounds. Flushed and sweaty, these two men faced the pressing horde of hissing, steaming, dusty rattletraps with the look of men who are struggling with a totally uncontrollable force that threatens to engulf them at any moment.

One blew his whistle in short, sharp blasts that matched every breath he took. With his left hand, he seemed to gather the cars in a steady hooking motion that pushed them on past his right hand, which moved like a piston in the air, shoving the heaps through the narrow gate. The other cop, taller and sadder, stood astride the center line of the asphalt road and glared slowly and deliberately at each car as it rolled past him.

The old man, by now totally hot under the collar, muttered barely audible obscenities as we drew abreast of the first cop.

"What was that, buddy?" The cop's voice was level

and menacing, cutting through the racket of the Pontiac's piston slap like an ice cube going down your back on a hot day. Instantly, an electric feeling of imminent danger whipped through the car. Even my brother stopped whining.

"Uh . . . pardon me, officer?" The old man had turned on his innocent voice, which always sounded a little like he was slightly hard of hearing. He stuck his head out the window with exaggerated politeness.

"Did I hear you call me a son of a bitch, buddy?" The tall cop was approaching the side of the car, his eyes piercing the old man like a pair of hot ice picks.

"Uh . . . what was that, officer? Sir?"

"You heard me." A hamlike hand rested authoritatively on the door handle; a heavy foot clunked solidly on the running board. The line came to a halt behind us.

"I'm sorry, officer. What was it you said, sir?"

"Did you call me a son of a bitch?"

"Oh, heavens no! Mercy me! Why, good gracious, you must have heard me sneeze. I am troubled with hay fever." The old man sounded amazingly like an Episcopalian minister.

He sneezed loudly into his sleeve as a demonstration. I had seen the old man get out of many a tight squeak before, but this performance topped them all. I drank it in, knowing what I was seeing a master at work. My mother said nothing through it all, just looked nervously pathetic, which seemed to help the old man's act.

"OK, buster. Just watch yer lip, y'hear?"

"Why, bless my buttons, officer, I certainly will. Yes,

indeed! That is fine advice. Heavens to Betsy, I certainly will."

With a flick of his wrist, the cop waved us on. The emergency was over. The old man let the clutch out so suddenly that the car jerked heavily twice before lurching forward.

An elderly, toilworn Chevy pickup truck carrying a farmer, his wife, seven kids and a Bluetick hound had stalled just ahead of us. The old man, out of pure reflex, muttered: "Son of a bitch!" Realizing he wasn't yet out of earshot, he covered it with a loud, juicy sneeze.

It grew hotter and hotter in our little oven as we waited for the farmer to get the Chevy moving again. At last we got inside the chicken-wire fence and past the little box office where they took the old man's two bucks, the price for an afternoon of untrammeled bliss.

My father shoved his hat onto the back of his head while he fished frantically inside his coat pocket for his pack of Luckies, a sure sign that he was reaching the boiling point.

"Holy Christ, wouldja look at that!"

Ahead of us, waves of heat rose from a long line of motionless cars that stretched toward the distant parking lot. They had the look of cars that hadn't moved for maybe two hours. People sat on running boards; fat ladies fanned themselves in the shade; kids ran in and out past spare tires and around radiators; and guys with pushcarts selling hot dogs and Fudgsicles moved up and down the line, doing a roaring business.

Two cars ahead of us, a lady was unpacking a lunch

basket and spreading bowls of potato salad and jars of pickles on a blanket that she'd laid by the cornfield. A tall man in shirt sleeves and a straw hat chomped contentedly on a sandwich.

"Would you kids like a peanut-butter sandwich?" My mother began rummaging in the paper bag that held our lunch.

To the left of the line of cars was a high board fence plastered with red-and-yellow posters. From behind it, suddenly, surged a tidal wave of deep-throated roaring, followed by clouds of dust and the smell of burning rubber and castor oil. My father hunched over the wheel in excitement. This was his home ground, and he could hardly wait to get in on the action.

SSSSSKKKKKRRRRREEEEEE . . . KABOOM!

For an instant, something blotted out the sun. One of the picnicking ladies stood frozen, holding a bowl of cole slaw. The sandwich eater stared heavenward, his mouth poised open in mid-chomp. The old man, who had just tilted a can of beer toward the sky, stopped short, foam dribbling down his shirt front, eyes bugging out in amazement and delight.

The top of the board fence disintegrated with a stupendous crash and there, gracefully airborne high above the line of jalopies, a bright-blue racing car with a big number 12 on its side arched overhead, trailing smoke. The white-helmeted driver, his green goggles glinting in the sun, looked perfectly calm. It was all in a day's work. One wheel flew crazily ahead of him on a solo flight.

61

"JESUS CHRIST! THERE GOES IRON MAN!" the old man yelled as his favorite member of the racing fraternity disappeared in a cloud of dust and oil spray into the cornfield off to our right.

A great cheer came from behind the shattered fence as the crowd roared its approval of Iron Man's spectacular crackup. That's what they came to see, and Iron Man gave it to them.

As the line of cars inched toward the parking lot, we could see a tow truck dragging Iron Man's lethal Kurtis-Offy Special back into the fray. Iron Man himself, wearing blue coveralls, sat nonchalantly in the cockpit, waving to the crowd. Dirt-track racers are not ordinary mortals.

"GO GET 'EM THE NEXT HEAT, IRON MAN!" bellowed the old man.

"Boy, ain't he a pisser?" This was my father's highest compliment.

"Little pitchers have big ears," my mother said again.

"Well, he is." My father knew a pisser when he saw one.

At last we were parked, between an ancient Willys-Knight and a Cord owned by a prominent local Mafia finger man who ran a mortuary on the side as a kind of tie-in.

"We'll meet you by the band shell," said the old man. He was in a hurry to get inside the arena.

"Now, you be careful," my mother told me, as she did so often. It was a phrase that ran like a litany through her life. She dragged my kid brother off in the direction of the quilt tent. My old man and I headed for the track.

Five minutes later, we were in the stands, immersed in the roaring mob that had come from miles around to cheer the mayhem and carnage on the dirt oval below. I sat hunched next to a gaunt, stringy, hawk-faced farmer who wore a broad-brimmed straw hat low over his eyes. His Adam's apple, as big as a turkey egg, bobbed up and down in excitement as he watched the racers. He rolled Bull Durham cigarettes automatically with his left hand as his elbow dug into my ribs. His wife, a large, pink, rubbery woman, breast-fed a baby as the races roared on.

Dirt-track racing is as much a part of an Indiana county fair as applesauce, pumpkins and pig judging. Down below us, Iron Man Gabruzzi—back in action, his famous blue Kurtis-Offy a little dented from the previous heat—battled it out with his archrival, Duke Grunion, who drove a battle-scarred yellow blown Ford special, and a field of lesser competitors. Round and round they careened, throwing up sheets of yellow dust laced with the blue smoke of burning oil and scorching tires. From time to time, a car would leave the pack, slewing sideways, and bounce into the rail, trailing even more smoke than usual. The mob leaped to its feet, bellowing bloodthirstily, and then squatted again, waiting for the next near catastrophe. Over it all, the tinny voice of the P.A. announcer kept up a running commentary of feeble jokes and trivial observations. Hot-dog vendors squeezed up

63

and down the rows, passing out the franks as fast as they could slap them between buns.

The old man was in seventh heaven, cheering wildly every time Iron Man moved ahead of Duke Grunion on the far turn to come whistling down the straight, his battered old Offy screaming. The 100-Mile Dirt Track Championship Race is as fiercely fought as any Grand Prix, and in some ways is far more exciting.

The last lap saw Iron Man and Duke battling it out on the homestretch, both sliding high on the banked oval, flat out, with Iron Man zooming across the finish line a half car ahead of Duke. The checkered flag rose and fell; the crowd cheered insanely as Iron Man, waving jauntily from his cockpit, took his victory lap, saluting the crowd. He had won 150 bucks for an afternoon's work in the hot sun.

We filed out of the stands and headed straight for the bandstand, which was at the center of the fairgrounds. Inside my head, the roaring of the race cars continued, blotting out the sound of the crowd. I would be hearing them in my sleep for at least a week. My nose burned from the gasoline and alcohol fumes.

"I gotta have a beer." Racing always made my father very thirsty.

We stopped at a stand while he guzzled a bottle of Blatz and listened to the other dirt-track fanatics yelling about how great the race had been. I drank a Nehi orange, my fifth of the day. Already my stomach was starting to ferment.

My mother and kid brother were waiting at the bandstand when we finally showed up.

"I gotta go to the toilet!" whined Randy. My brother always had to go to the toilet, especially when there was no toilet around. On either side of us, open sheds filled with rows of soft-eyed cows and jostling farmers stretched into the distance.

"Go behind that truck. I'll stand guard." The old man had handled this situation many times. My brother scooted behind the truck and emerged a couple of minutes later, sheepishly.

"I wanna see the pigs!" he said.

"So do I," I seconded him. I always liked to look at pigs, and still do, for that matter. There is something very satisfying about the way a pig looks. They were housed in a tent next to the cows, which were kind of dull. Row on row, the porkers lounged casually, completely at ease with the world. I have never understood why the pig is an animal whose name is used in derision. He is intelligent and kindly, often benevolent, in fact; in short, totally with it.

In the center of the tent, under floodlights, an enormous white hog with black spots graciously accepted the applause of his admirers. GRAND CHAMPION, the sign read, and above his bed of straw hung a large, trailing blue ribbon attached to a blue-and-gold rosette. Below it was a plaque: BIG HORACE. He had eaten half the ribbon. His tiny red eyes peered out at us jocularly. He was a champion and he knew it. Lesser pigs grunted and rooted in pens all around, but Big Horace was the star. We stood silently before this regal beast for several minutes.

"I bet that baby'd make great bacon," my father finally said in a quiet voice. A look of reproach flickered over Horace's mighty face as he glanced in our direction.

We moved on with the crowd into the prize-goat tent. Photographers were popping flashbulbs around a luxuriant, silken-haired Angora with a set of wicked-looking horns. Beside him stood a short, fat 4-H girl wearing a green beret and holding up another blue ribbon. The goat tent was among the gamier exhibits, but exciting. Goats are unpredictable, and from time to time one would try to climb out and go after some kid's taffy apple. Goats always have fancy names. This one was Prince Bernadotte Charlemagne d'Alexandre of Honeyvale Farms. The 4-H girl stared solemnly at the cameras while the bulbs popped on. The goat just chewed and looked bored.

We wandered along with the dusty crowds, looking at turkeys, ducks, rabbits, sheep, guinea pigs and chickens. It was in the chicken tent that an enigmatic event took place. In one corner, a heavy-set lady wearing a green shawl sat on a camp chair next to a large, fancy cage containing a single white, efficient-looking chicken. Atop the cage was a sign: ESMERALDA KNOWS.

"Would you folks care to have Esmeralda tell your fortune?"

"Yeah! Yeah! I want my fortune told! Waaaaaa!" My kid brother went into high gear. The chicken hopped around in the cage and clucked knowingly.

"How much is it?" asked my mother warily.

"Only a dime. Just ten cents to learn the little boy's fortune."

The chicken pecked at the cage, waiting to go to work. My mother reached into her carryall with the picture of Carmen Miranda on it, fished out a dime and handed it to my brother, who grabbed it eagerly.

"Put the dime into the slot, little boy, and watch the chicken tell your fortune."

My brother walked up to the cage, his face inches away from the chicken's beak. The two stared at each other for a long moment.

A small crowd was beginning to gather. He dropped the dime into the slot on the side of the cage. At that, a ladder dropped from the roof inside the cage. The chicken scurried up rung by rung, clucking madly. At the top of the ladder was a box containing folded slips of paper. The chicken picked one out with its beak, hopped back down the ladder, eyes rolling wildly, and dropped the slip of paper into a chute, releasing a half-dozen grains of corn.

Cluck-cluck-cluck waaaaaak! It gulped them down hungrily.

"There. Esmeralda has told your fortune," the lady said to my brother. I noticed that she had a mustache.

The slip of paper had dropped into a small tray outside the cage. My brother grabbed it and read the message aloud:

"'You are unwise in your in-vest-ments. Care in the future will ensure your success.'"

67

My mother laughed. "Esmeralda was right. You spent your entire allowance last week on Fudgsicles. See?"

My brother glared angrily at Esmeralda. After that, I had no desire to hear any smart talk from Esmeralda about *my* life.

"OK, you've had your fun. Now there's something *I* gotta see," said my father. "Wait'll you see this. I read about it in the paper."

"What now?" asked my mother as we started after him. She knew better than to fight the inevitable.

"Hairy Gertz saw it yesterday and he said you wouldn't believe it."

"Well," said my mother, "if Hairy Gertz said that, it certainly *must* be something!"

"What do you mean by that?" my father shot back. Hairy Gertz was one of the old man's bowling buddies, famed throughout the county for his collection of incredibly gross jokes. My mother didn't answer.

"Anyway, I want to see it." He went over to a dozing cop and asked him directions.

My father came back, beaming. "OK, here we go. Follow me." We did, and a couple of minutes later were waiting in line in front of another tent.

"Wait'll you see this. You won't believe it!" My father rubbed his hands together in anticipation. The crowd snaked into the tent in a long line. Finally, we were inside.

Big floodlights hung from the tent poles. In the middle of the sawdust floor, there was a roped-off square.

"What is it?" my mother asked as soon as she got a look at what was on the platform.

"What do you mean, 'What is it?' Can't you read the sign, stupid?"

A sign hung over the astounding object that had moved even Hairy Gertz to speechless wonder. The crowd stood in reverent silence. Occasionally, someone snapped a picture with a Brownie, hoping that there was enough light to enable him to preserve this magnificent exhibit forever in his book of memories. The sign, hand lettered in gilt on fake parchment, was draped with an American flag. It read:

THIS GIANT 47-POUND, 10-OUNCE INDIANA PUMPKIN, BEARING A STRIKING LIKENESS TO OUR BELOVED PRESIDENT FRANKLIN DELANO ROOSEVELT, WAS GROWN BY HOMER L. SEASTRUNK OF R.F.D. 2, NEW JERUSALEM, INDIANA. MR. SEASTRUNK PLANS TO PRESENT THE PUMPKIN TO PRESIDENT ROOSEVELT.

"How d'y like that?" my father said softly as the four of us stood before the great pumpkin.

Someone behind me muttered angrily, "That nut is ruinin' the country. I know what *I'd* do with that pumpkin!"

"Shhhhh!" several indignant patriots hissed back.

There was no doubt that it was one of the high points of the fair. Another sign said that Mr. Seastrunk himself would make a personal appearance at three P.M. to give a short talk on how he figured God had created that pumpkin in honor of the President. He would also give free autographs.

"I told you this was worth seeing," said my father as he wound one of the knobs on his trusty camera. "Now, how wouldja like to go next door and see the world's biggest cheese?"

The same cheese, I have no doubt, has been on exhibit at every fair I ever attended. It wasn't much to look at; when you've seen one, you've seen them all, even if it weighs two tons. A sign read: THE MILK FROM 2000 COWS FOR ONE FULL YEAR WAS REQUIRED TO MAKE THIS CHEESE. IT WOULD MAKE OVER 422,000 CHEESE SAND-WICHES.

This kind of stuff really got to the old man. He snapped more pictures and walked all the way around the cheese, examining it from every angle. All it did was make my kid brother hungry again.

It was late in the afternoon now and the crowd was really warmed up, moving in straggly columns around huge, black-wheeled tractors, cultivators, threshing machines and other agricultural exotica. Salesmen, the collars of their shirts opened, ties hanging limply, shouted over bullhorns as we wandered dazedly amid the shuffling throng, kicking up bread crusts and paper cups as we eddied on.

"I'm hungry," my brother droned, his voice barely audible above the uproar.

"You've just gone. You'll have to wait," said my mother, pushing the damp hair back off her forehead.

"I don't have to go! I'm *hungry!*" Randy never gave up.

"You heard what your mother said." My father got into the act.

"I said I'm HUNGRY!"

"You're *what?* You've had three taffy apples, four hot dogs and two root beers. That's enough for a while."

"I wanna PICKLE!"

As it happened, we were passing a stand where a guy in a red vest and a white chef's hat was selling giant dark-green pickles from barrels. People eat strange stuff at county fairs.

"I want one, too!" I said.

We all bought pickles in wax paper and rejoined the moiling mob. My pickle must have weighed two pounds. Every time I bit into it, it squirted down the front of my shirt.

It was getting dark now and 50 times more exciting as the bright lights began to flash on. I washed down the tart, puckery taste of the pickle with some cold butter-milk from a paper cup with a picture on it of a red cow wearing a green hat. My knees had begun to ache from the endless trudging through sawdust and over piles of debris. On either side of us, a sparkling ribbon of spinning yellow wheels, blue-white neon lights and hot orange flames under cooking grills stretched to the horizon. Guys with leather jackets and great mops of carefully combed, greasy hair ranged through the crowds, looking for fights and girls.

71

On a high platform, two blondes wearing silver helmets sat on the saddles of enormous bright-red Harley-
Davidsons. They gunned the motors deafeningly sending thin blue exhaust smoke into the crowd that stood
around the platform with glazed eyes and gaping mouths.

"Dee-fying death every second, straight from the world
championships in Paris, France, Melba and Bonnie stare
into the very jaws of eternity!" yelled the barker.

BBBBRRRROOOOOOOMMMMMMM!BAAAARRR-
OOOOOOOMMMM! Another cloud of acrid smoke
drifted out over the mob.

The barker spieled on: "There is time for just one
more big show tonight, just one more! Never in your life
have you seen anything to equal THE DEVIL RIDE!"

BAAARRROOOOOOM! BBBBBRRRRRRROOOOOO-
OMMMMM!

"Bee-ginning in just one minute. In just sixty seconds!
Beautiful Melba and lovely Bonnie stare into the jaws
of death!"

The two blondes, thin-faced and pallid, peered out
from under their spectacular helmets, chewing gum steadily as they gunned their Harleys.

"I gotta see that!" This act was *designed* for my old
man. Anything that had to do with roaring motors and
crash helmets hit him in the vitals. Add the fact that
these were skinny blonde women, another weakness,
and you had bigtime showbiz, as far as he was concerned.

With a couple of final, provocative roars, the two raced
down the ramp and disappeared through a doorway

outlined in yellow with a string of colored light bulbs festooning a blood-red Devil's face with green eyes.

We followed close behind my father as he elbowed his way through the sweaty throng of daredevil fans to the head of the line inside the tent. We found ourselves standing at the rim of a circular pit ten or fifteen feet deep. The noise was deafening; the wooden floor vibrated and creaked under our feet. The air was thick with burning gasoline. Down in the pit, the two motorcycles boomed round and round, chasing each other madly in faster and faster circles, rising up the curved walls until they were riding almost horizontally under the chicken wire that separated the Harleys from us.

A white-faced, blue-veined minister, his high collar spotted with catsup, stood next to us in tense excitement. Kids ran wildly in and out of the crowd, throwing peanut shells at the riders as they screamed round and round in their tight spiral. The old man peered down into the maelstrom, pounding the rail in excitement as the motorcycles accelerated faster and faster.

"DEFYING GRAVITY ON THEIR SPECIALLY BUILT HARLEY-DAVIDSONS, MELBA AND BONNIE WILL NOW PERFORM A DEATH-DEFYING FEAT NEVER BEFORE SEEN IN THE UNITED STATES!" shouted the voice on the P.A. system over the racket. Down in the gloom of the hell pit, the exhausts trailed smoke as the motorcycles rode abreast.

"MELBA AND BONNIE WILL CHANGE MOTOR-CYCLES AT TOP SPEED!"

73

The crowd hunched forward with expectancy. Even the kids were quiet. The thunder of the motorcycles had reached the point where no more sound could be endured. The whole structure—the floor, the guy wires, the back teeth, everything—vibrated to the scream of the Harleys. Down in the pit, there was a quick shuffling of bodies and it was done.

"Fer Chrissake, how d'y like that! I wouldna' believed it!" said the oldman to no one in particular. The minister, his black hat hanging at a rakish angle, applauded frantically.

Once again we were out on the midway, 50 cents poorer but infinitely richer in worldly experience.

My mother, who was eating a piece of watermelon, said plaintively, "I haven't seen the quilts yet."

"I wanna go on the Ferris wheel," whined my brother for the 298th time.

"I thought you were gonna see 'em when we went to the races," said the old man, ignoring him for the 298th time.

"We went to the cookie tasting instead."

"The what?"

"The cookie tasting. Over by where they were having the artistic flower arranging."

The old man said nothing and headed for a three-story-high orange face that laughed madly under a sign that read FUN HOUSE. He hoped that by not answering, she would forget the quilts.

"Mrs. Wimple has a quilt in this year," she persisted. "Bernice Wimple, from the club."

74

My mother belonged to a dart-ball club that staged mysterious contests in the church basement every Thursday. Bernice Wimple played for the La Porte, Indiana, Bearcats, a legendary dart-ball team.

"It's a Thomas Jefferson quilt," she continued, wiping a watermelon seed off her chin with a paper napkin that said HAVE FUN in blue letters over an American flag.

My father, realizing he'd have to say *something*, stalled for time: "What the hell kinda quilt is that?"

"Well, it's a patriotic quilt that has the face of Thomas Jefferson on it, done in cross-stitch."

"Oh, well! *That* I gotta see!" said my father sarcastically.

After a ten-minute search, we finally found the tent with the quilt exhibit, under strings of yellow light bulbs. The quilts were tacked up all around, stretched tight, so that their designs could be admired respectfully from behind a rope by the motley throng of art lovers. Mrs. Wimple's entry was among them. We stood before the 6'×9' portrait.

"He looks a little cross-eyed to me," the old man observed accurately.

"I think it's very pretty. Mrs. Wimple worked seven years on it."

We peered at the third-place ribbon it sported and moved on to look at the others. The winning quilt had a stand to itself. It bore a spectacular portrait of Old Faithful on a yellow background framed by purple mountains and surrounded by a herd of animals: a moose, an elk, two bighorn sheep, a bunny with pink eyes and what appeared to be a hippopotamus. Above this scene in Old English-style red, white and blue letters was the following profundity:

The Beauty of Our Glorious Land Is Surpassed Only by God's Blessed Handiwork.
—Roswell T. Blount, L.L.D.

"Now, that's what I call pretty," said my father solemnly, reading the inscription. We all agreed that it was pretty.

Most of the quilts ran heavily to such patriotic themes, except for one that had a ribbon for UNUSUAL SUBJECT— HONORABLE MENTION. It was a full-color portrait done on a background of grass green. The eyes of the subject, staring beadily out from under his familiar cap, stopped the old man dead in his tracks.

"Well, I'll be damned. I'll be a son of a bitch!"

We stood in awe before this transcendent work of art.

"I never thought I'd see Luke Appling on a *quilt!*"

Sure enough, it was a ruddy likeness of old Luke himself, the foul-ball king of the American League. My father, a lifelong Chicago White Sox fan, was visibly moved. Under the picture streamed the legend, woven in golden thread:

BATTLING LUKE APPLING

ALWAYS FIRST IN OUR HEARTS

(I wonder what a genuine Luke Appling quilt would go for today in the chic, high-camp *boutiques* along Third Avenue in Manhattan.)

"Let's go, all you great lovers, all you he-men," barked a man in a purple derby at the next concession. "Let's see what kind of man you really are. Show that beautiful girl you're with just what kind of man you really are. Here you are, here you are, here you are, here's your chance to get up and really ring the bell. Everybody wins. It's good healthful exercise and everybody wins. Ring the bell. I said everybody wins. All right, you lovers, show that little lady what kind of muscles you really got. Ring the bell."

We joined a circle of gawkers at the foot of a 30-foot pole that had a wire running up its length, with a big gong at the top. At the bottom was a round metal plate. The pole, candy-striped red and white, was marked with gradations. Beginning at the bottom, they read:

CASPAR MILQUETOAST

LADIES' DIVISION

BETTER EAT YOUR WHEATIES

AVERAGE

NOT BAD

WATCH OUT FOR THIS GUY

And way up at the top: wow! A REAL HE-MAN.

A huge, rosy-cheeked, curly-haired tractor-driver type, wearing Sears, Roebuck pants and a checkered cowboy shirt, stepped into the arena.

"Let's see how the young man swings. Look at those shoulders, folks, look at those arms! Swing the hammer nice and smooth; hit it right on the button. Let's see you ring the bell."

The barker handed the behemoth a big mallet. His friends jeered and snorted noisily in derision.

"Belt the hell out of it, Caleb!" one yelled.

"Aw, come on. He cain't make it past the LADIES' mark. He ain't got no lead in his pencil!"

The crowd snickered contemptuously. Caleb grabbed the handle and swung wildly. K-THUNK! The iron weight rose feebly up the cable and fell back with a clank.

"No wonder yew cain't make out with Minnie!" hooted one of his friends.

Caleb spat on his hands, swung again. The hammer whistled. KER-THUNK!

The weight rose higher this time, almost reaching the AVERAGE mark halfway up the pole. Caleb looked thoughtful, as the distant sound of the merry-go-round calliope switched from *Alexander's Ragtime Band* to *The Valkyrie*. It was, indeed, a Wagnerian moment, the twilight of the gods.

He peered upward at the gong, which now seemed twice as high as it had before. He kicked the dirt like a batter digging in at the batter's box, wiped his hands on his trousers and once again grabbed the mallet. His biceps rippled under the tight-fitting cowboy shirt. Dark circles of sweat stained the armpits. His back arched. This time, he swung the hammer from the ground, then

78

up in a great, swinging arc. K-THUNK! The metal weight drifted up the wire, slowed and stopped at CASPAR MILQUE-TOAST.

"Man, yew better quit before that thing don't move at all!"

Caleb dropped the hammer, his face bathed in sweat and red from humiliation, paid the barker and left the arena, a broken man. I had a suspicion of what was going to happen next. If there was ever a sucker for that kind of thing, it was my old man.

"I think I'm gonna try whacking that thing," he whispered.

"Now, don't make a fool of yourself." My mother was always afraid of his making a fool of himself. She had good reason to be.

"Aw, just for fun. I mean, what the hell."

"All right, you lovers, you saw cousin Caleb get all the way up there to AVERAGE. Let's see how you can do. Ring the bell, ring the bell, who can ring the bell?"

As Caleb snarled at the Greek chorus of hisses and boos from his corn-liquored buddies, the old man stepped into the clearing without a word, gave the guy a quarter, grabbed the hammer and swung. K-THWACK! He didn't hit it with anywhere near the thump that Caleb got into her. But: ZZZIIIIIIIP . . . BONG!

The iron weight raced to the top and rang the bell so loud it could be heard a block away.

"Y'see that, Caleb? That there guy's got lead in *his* pencil!" The nasal bray of rustic wit opened up again.

"The little man wins a box of genuwine Swiss-choco-

79

late bonbons. All ya gotta do is have a good swing. Who's gonna win the next big prize, all you lovers?"

My father, stunned at his totally unprecedented success, grabbed the box of chocolates amid the applause of the rabble.

The last we saw of Caleb was the hammer rising and falling at two bits a swing, being milked by that barker for every cent he owned.

This moment was to become a sacred gem in the family archives. The more it was told, the greater the feat became. Caleb grew into Paul Bunyan, and the old man's hammer swing rose to Olympic proportions. It wasn't until I was 16 that I read an article in *Popular Mechanics* and discovered that the barker operated the thing with his foot. The old man, fortunately, never found out.

As we moved from one marvel to the next, my brother and I began to list heavily to starboard; we hadn't stopped eating since we stepped onto the fairgrounds: homemade popcorn balls, red, white and blue, made by the 4-H; girl-scout cookies; French fries; boiled corn on the cob dripping butter; Nehi orange and Hires root beer; peanuts; pumpkin pie; hot dogs; pickles; American Legion Auxiliary crullers; baked beans on paper plates; lemonade; Ladies of the Moose angel-food cake; taffy apples; and a thousand free samples, including Purina Chick Chow, which my brother and I both ate avidly. Added to this was the real specialty of any Indiana fair—homemade black-walnut chocolate fudge, displayed in thick, fly-crawling slabs at stands operated by beaming Kiwanians wearing funny hats and badges. We also scoffed down about five pounds each of peculiarly native candy called vanilla angel breath, an airy concoction so cloyingly sweet that a bite-sized portion could rot teeth at 50 paces. A fundamental ground rule of the county fair was that kids could have anything they wanted to eat, just this once. Steadily, we chewed our way toward Armageddon.

Barkers on all sides hawked everything from horse collars to Mystic Mohegan Indian Squaw Korn Kure. We paused briefly while my old man hurled lumpy baseballs at battered wooden milk bottles, his blood rising visibly as the balls bounced off the canvas at the rear of the tent. Other athletes strained and grunted, their hard-earned cash winging into the canvas with dull thuds. A shelf held the possible booty: cerise Kewpie dolls with enormous red-feather fans, stuffed pandas, shiny china panthers with clocks in their stomachs, souvenir ashtrays in the shape of mother-of-pearl toilets—a veritable king's ransom.

The proprietor, a short, round man with a gray chin, played them like rainbow trout. "Y'got a nice arm, son. Let's see you lay it in there. Show the little lady how the big-leaguers do it. Look at that arm, folks! He's tossin' a real knuckler. Three balls for a quarter. How 'bout you, little lady? Try yer luck."

While my father was winding up, the man handed three baseballs to a skinny girl about 11 years old. She quickly bowled over three milk bottles and still had a ball left.

"Pick any prize y'want, little lady, any prize!"

81

The sweating yahoos threw with renewed vigor, dollar bills cascading across the counter. The 11-year-old picked a Kewpie doll and left. It wasn't until the next day that we found out she was the daughter of the guy who ran the joint. We saw them in Joe's Diner eating shredded wheat.

It was getting late. Our feet were coated with chewing gum and popcorn, and we were covered with a thick layer of finely powdered yellow clay. I knew that somewhere on the grounds Schwartz and Flick and Kissel were doing things that they would lie to me about the next day.

Now we were deep in the heart of the thrill-ride section of the fair. The Ferris wheel reached high up into the dark sky, its spokes outlined in colored light bulbs, jerking upward and stopping and jerking and jerking upward again. It loomed over us like a huge illuminated snowflake.

"I wanna go on the Ferris wheel!" Randy whined for the 317th time. This time, he was not to be denied.

My father bought a ticket from the man in the little booth. Off my brother went through the turnstile and into a wobbly car the color of a grape. A minute later, he was laughing down at us and sticking his tongue out as he swept up ecstatically into the night. Every few seconds, the wheel would stop and unload a car. We stood around and waved every time he went past.

Finally, the grape car stopped at the bottom. We could see the attendant in blue coveralls swing the gate open. He seemed to be arguing with the occupant. The attendant finally hollered out to the guy in the box office:

"HEY, JAKE! THIS KID WON'T GET OUT!"

"Oh, fer Chrissake, what now?" the old man muttered.

"NOW, YOU GET OUT. YOU HAD ENOUGH," said the attendant.

"WHAAAAAAAA!"

The attendant reached in and wrenched him out, fighting and kicking every inch of the way. My father took over the battle, dragging him out into the midway.

"I WANNA GO ON AGAIN!!" he screamed, but to no avail.

The big wheel started up without him as we moved on to the next attraction, Randy struggling at every step.

We tried to hurry past a merry-go-round swarming with little kids and mothers, but it was no use. Randy threatened to throw himself under it if he didn't get to ride on it. I stood with my father as he whirled round and round beside my mother, sitting on a black swan with a yellow beak. He tried to do a headstand as *The Man on the Flying Trapeze* played over and over and over and over. After the sixth ride, we managed to pull him off. He emerged slightly pale but still game. We ate a red candy cane apiece, thus setting the stage for total disaster.

My father never went on rides unless they were real gut busters. He had ventured unflinchingly onto roller coasters so violent as to turn away strong men, quaking in fear. He spotted one of his old favorites, an evil contraption known as the Whirligig Rocket Whip. We had been warned of its presence long before we arrived on the scene. Screams of horror and the flashing light of the emergency ambulance led us to the killer ride of them all.

At every fair or amusement park, there is one ride that is the yokel equivalent of the main bull ring in Madrid. This is where callow-faced youths and gorilla-armed icemen prove their virility to their admiring women. The Rocket Whip was a classic of its kind. It consisted of two bullet-shaped cars, one yellow, one red, attached to the ends of rotating arms. It revolved simultaneously clockwise and up and down. At the same time, the individual cars rotated in their own orbits. The old man, spotting the Rocket Whip, strained forward like a fire horse smelling smoke.

"Are you sure you should go on that?" My mother held back.

"Aw, come on. It'll do the kids good. Blow the stink off 'em." She didn't answer, just gazed up in fear at the mechanical devil that was now about to take on passengers. The yellow car rested near the ground, it's wire-mesh door invitingly open.

He bought three tickets from the operator, who sat near the turnstile in a rocking chair, the control lever at his side.

"Let's go, kids."

We piled into the car. It was simplicity itself; two hard metal seats and a bar that clamped down over the laps of the occupants, so that their bodies didn't become actually dismembered. We sat stationary for a long moment. High above us, the occupants of the red car gazed down at us—upside down—waiting for Thor's hammer to descend.

The man yanked the lever and it began. Slowly at first, we began to spin. The landscape outside our wire-mesh cage blurred as we gained speed. We leaped skyward, up, up; paused briefly at the top of the arc at what looked like thousands of feet above ground level, then plunged straight down. Just as we neared the earth, we were whipped upward again. By this time, the car, caught by enormous forces, had begun spinning centrifugally on its own. We were trapped in a giant cream separator.

There were brief flashes of dark sky, flashing lights, gaping throngs, my old man's rolling eyes, his straw hat sailing around the interior of the car.

"Oh, no, fer Chrissake!" he yelled. A shower of loose change—quarters, nickels, dimes, pennies—sprayed out of his pockets, filled the car for an instant and was gone, spun out into the night.

"Oh, Jesus Christ! No!" he yelled again, as his brown-and-white marbled Wearever fountain pen with his name on it, given to him by the bowling team, flew out of his pocket and disappeared into the night.

Higher and higher we flew, swooping low to scream upward again. My kid brother, chalk white, whimpered piteously. I hung onto the iron bar, certain that my last hour had arrived. My head thumped the back of the car steadily as it spun.

"Ain't this fun, kids? Wow, what a ride!" shouted

the old man, sweating profusely. He made a grab for his hat as it sailed past.

"Wave to Ma, kids! There she is!"

It was then that the operator turned the power on full. Everything that had gone before was only a warm-up. Our necks snapped back as the Rocket Whip accelerated. I was not touching the seat at any point. Jack-knifed over the bar, I saw that one of my shoes had been wrenched off my foot. At that moment, with no warning, my kid brother let it all go. His entire day's accumulation of goodies, now marinated and pungent, gushed out in a geyser. The car spun crazily. The air was filled with atomized spray of everything he had ingested for the past 24 hours. Down we swooped.

"My new pongee shirt!"

Soaked from head to foot, the old man struggled frantically in his seat to get out of the line of fire. It was no use. I felt it coming, too. I closed my eyes and the vacuum forces of outer space just dragged it all out of me like a suction pump. From a million miles away, I heard my old man shouting something, but it didn't matter. All I knew was that if I didn't hold onto that bar, it would be all over.

We gradually spun to a stop and finally the wire-mesh door opened. My feet touched the blessed earth. On rubbery legs, clinging weakly together, the three of us tottered past the turnstile as other victims were clamped into the torture chamber we had just left.

"Great ride, eh, folks? I left you on a little longer, 'cause I could see the kids was really enjoyin' it," said

86

the operator, pocketing the last of my father's change as we passed through the turnstile.

"Thanks. It sure was great," said the old man with a weak smile, a bent cigarette hanging from his lips. He always judged a ride by how sick it made him. The nausea quotient of the Rocket Whip was about as high as they come.

We sat on a bench for a while to let the breeze dry off the old man's shirt, and so that our eyes could get back into focus. From all around us we could hear the whoops and hollers of people going up and down and sideways on the other rides.

There was one across from the Rocket Whip that my kid brother, who had great recuperative powers, *had* to go on. We didn't have the strength to stop him. It was a big barrel made out of some kind of shiny metal and it spun around like a cocktail shaker on its side. The people were screaming and yelling; their skirts were flying up, their shoes falling off. Randy loved it. We hung around and waited until they threw him out.

It was late now and getting a little chilly. It seemed like we had been at the fair for about a month. We sat on the bench while the crowd trudged past us, chewing hot dogs, lugging jars of succotash that they had bought at the exhibits, twirling sticks with little yellow birds on the ends of strings that we could hear whistling over the calliope on the merry-go-round, wearing souvenir Dr. Bodley's Iron Nerve Tonic sun visors, carrying drunken cousins who had hit the applejack since early morning, wheeling reeking babies smeared with caked Pablum and chocolate. Long-legged, skinny, yellow dogs with their tongues hanging out kept running back and forth and barking. It had been an unforgettable day.

"It sure feels good to just sit for a while," said my mother as she took off one shoe and dumped out some popcorn. The old man didn't say anything. The unlit cigarette still in his mouth, he just sat and watched the crowd move on, with his hat pushed back on his head. We sat like that for about 15 minutes, getting our wind back.

"Did you feel a drop of rain?" My mother looked up at the black sky and held out her hand.

The old man looked up. "Nah. You must be sweating."

"*I* felt a drop," I said, sticking my hand out.

The only one who didn't stick his hand out was my kid brother, who didn't care whether it rained or not. He just squatted at the end of the bench and went back to whining, which he always did when there was nothing else to do.

"Stop that! You're getting on my nerves!" said my mother, poking him in the ribs to shut him up.

"I'm tired." He had that high-pitched, irritating sound that he was so good at.

"You know, I think it *is* raining." The old man made it official.

People started to hold newspapers over their heads and duck under awnings and into tents.

"Well, we might as well call it a day," announced the old man as he stood up and stuck his shirttail back into his pants.

"Let's head for the car."

We were a long way from the parking lot, which was over on the other side of the race track, about four miles away. We slogged doggedly through drifting mountains of candy wrappers, cigar butts, apple cores and cow flop; past tents full of canned lima beans and crocheted doilies, sweetheart pillows and gingerbread men, past shooting galleries and harvester machines and, finally, as the rain was really beginning to come down hard, we reached the car. We joined the procession of mud-splattered vehicles inching painfully, bumper to bumper, toward the distant highway.

"Y'know, I think the fair was even better than usual this year." My father said the same thing every year.

"Yes, the quilts *were* better this year," my mother agreed. "I think Bernice should have won at least second prize, though. The quilt that won wasn't that good."

"Oh, well, you know there's a lot of politics in that quilt business." The old man always figured there was politics in everything.

"I'm hungry!" Randy was at it again. He'd had an empty stomach ever since the Rocket Whip.

"We'll all have meat-loaf sandwiches when we get home," said my mother, wiping the steam off the inside of the windshield with her handkerchief, so that she could see out.

.   .   .

A Right Guard commercial featuring two French Foreign Legionnaires hiding behind a sand dune snapped me back to the real world. I glanced at my watch. My

God! It was 20 after four. Another goddamn night shot in front of the television set.

The closing credits of the movie came on, superimposed over the never-never dreamworld of Dick Haymes' state fair. I stood up, my knees cracking like twin castanets —an occupational hazard of late-late movie addiction. Hobbling over to the set, I reached down and snapped it off. The picture quickly shrank to a tiny dot in the middle of the gray screen. It lingered for a moment, glowing at me accusingly, as though I had killed it, and then disappeared.

I was ready to hit the sack. Or was I? No, there was something I had to do. What was it? I felt a peculiar, unnamable yearning from deep within me, a gnawing emptiness. I snacked my lips, and suddenly I knew. Marching purposefully to the front closet, I threw on my coat and headed out the front door into the empty streets on a lonely quest. I had to have a taffy apple.

SCUT FARKAS AND THE
MURDEROUS MARIAH

"I'm going to throw this wagon out, George. You don't play with it anymore, you're a general now. It's just gathering dust in the cellar. And if you don't want that little hatchet you got for your birthday, I'll get rid of that, too. I don't want it just banging around the house. It's liable to cause more trouble."

I am hearing George Washington's mother speaking in a quavery, old-timy voice, filtering through the hazy mists of past ages. There in the case right in front of my eyes was a stylish, archaic, hunched-up kind of cart with big spoked wheels. You could even see vestigial flecks of ancient red paint. The card read:

TOY WAGON GENERALLY SUPPOSED TO HAVE BELONGED TO GEORGE WASHINGTON AS A CHILD. THIS PRICELESS RELIC HAS BEEN ALMOST CONCLUSIVELY AUTHENTI-CATED.

93

George Washington's little red wagon! My mind boggled at the thought of the Father of Our Country tugging his high-spoked wooden toy through the boondocks, his 18th Century overalls faintly damp, his 18th Century kidshoes trailing laces in the sand, on his way to becoming the most successful revolutionist in all history.

I moved among the museum exhibits, now deep in a maelstrom of contemplation, mining a new vein of thought that had never occurred to me. In the next case, resting on a chaste velvet-covered podium, lay a chewed and worn wooden top of the type commonly known among the wooden-top set of my day as a spikesie. For the unfortunates unfamiliar with this maddening device, which over the centuries has separated the men from the boys among kids, a spikesie is a highly functional top-shaped wooden toy, beautifully, malevolently tapered down to a glittering steel spikelike spinning surface.

I stopped dead in my tracks, unable to believe my eyes. I looked long and hard, peering intently into the shiny glass case at the squat toy that was displayed there. There was no doubt about it. This was no ordinary spikesie, but identical with a sinister breed of top that I myself had once encountered. Bending low over the exhibit, I examined the inscription:

UNUSUAL HANDMADE TOP. ORIGIN UNKNOWN. SAID TO HAVE BEEN OWNED BY THE YOUNG THOMAS JEFFERSON.

My God! Thomas Jefferson! The elegant, consummate product of the age of reason; architect, statesman, utopian, man of letters. I wondered modestly whether I could have shown Tom a thing or two about top spinning. After all, a Declaration of Independence is one thing; a split top is another. The top rested quietly on its podium, mute and mysterious. It was a dark, rich, worn russet color. I wondered what its name was and what battles it had fought for the framer of the American way of life, what battles it had fought in the distant past and perhaps would fight again.

As I gazed at the top, old spike wounds itched vaguely beneath my tapered Italian slacks—old wounds I had sustained in hand-to-hand spikesie combat with antagonists of my dim past. Well did I remember Junior Kissel's economical, slicing sidearm movement, his green top string snapping curtly as he laid his yellow spikesie down right on a dime with a hissing whir. Flick, on the other hand —more erratic, more flamboyant—had a tendency to loft his spikesie, releasing it after a showy, looping overhand motion a good two feet above the surface of the playing field. His top spun with an exhibitionistic, wobbling playfulness and usually bounced hesitantly two or three times before settling into the groove. I myself preferred a sneaky, snakelike, underhand movement, beginning at the hip, swinging down to around the knees, upward slightly, and then the quick release after a fast, whiplike follow-through. Flick was great to watch; Kissel, methodical and clean. I was deadly.

In my day, there were two types of top spinners: those who merely *played* with a top—dilettantes, haphazard, sloppy, beneath notice; and those to whom a

95

top was a weapon in the purest sense, an extension of the will, an instrument of talent and aggression. Anything *but* a toy. I was one of that lonely breed. In combat, the top was used for only one thing: destruction. A top in the sweaty, tense hand of a real artist was capable of splitting his rival's top down the middle in the flickering of an eyelash.

I remember all too well the sinking sensation of total defeat when my first top skittered into the gutter, wobbling crazily like a drunken thing, in two distinct and irrevocable halves; and Scut Farkas, pocketing his sleek, ugly, black spikesie, strode away without so much as a backward glance. Then and there, the course of the next few years of my festering life was uncompromisingly set. In the secrecy of the basement, hour after hour, I clandestinely practiced every known motion, ranging from the rarely seen, difficult-to-master whiplash to the effete, delicate sidearm slice. Slowly my own true personal form began to emerge—until one spring day, in five minutes, I had halved the prized possessions of three of my closest friends. I knew then that I was ready for the big time.

Not quite. True, as a performer I felt fairly confident. It was the top itself that I lacked. To the untutored eye, I suppose, a top is a top—some red, some green, some blue. I find this hard to believe, but no doubt this is so to some. Ignorance may be bliss, but it is also pitiable. To the uninformed, all bats used by ballplayers look alike. This could not be further from the truth. Major-leaguers make annual treks to Louisville, Kentucky, for the sole and express purpose of selecting the seasoned lumber, the delicate taper, the precise finish and exquisitely calculated weight of the one thing that stands between them and anonymity. They guard their personal weapons with a fierce and unremitting jealousy. Long winter evenings are spent by internationally known sluggers resting before the fireside, carefully, endlessly rubbing next season's lumber with oily pork-chop bones, until finally, by opening day, the cleanup man steps to the plate, whipping through the ambient air a personal and completely assimilated fusion of man and device. Boog Powell's bat is as different from, say, Tony Conigliaro's as twilight is from dawn. They may look a little alike, but they don't feel the same.

Scut Farkas' top, known throughout the neighborhood as Mariah, had at least 50 or more confirmed kills to its credit, as well as half a dozen probables and God knows how many disabling gashes and wounds. Rumor held that this top had been owned by Farkas' father before him, a silent, steely-eyed, blue-jawed man who spoke with a thick, guttural accent. He ran a junk yard piled high with rotting hulks of deceased automobiles and rusting railroad-train wheels. Some said that it was not a top at all, but some kind of foreign knife, and not large, as tops go, being of a peculiar squat shape, a kind of small, stunted, pitch-black mushroom, wider above than most and sloping off quickly to a dark-blue, casehardened, glittering saber tip. Not only was the top strange in appearance; it spun with a mean, low humming—a truly distinctive, ominous note, a note that rose and fell, deep and rumbling, like the sound of an approaching squadron of distant Fokkers bent on death and destruction. Farkas, like all true professionals, rarely showed his top unless in anger. Skulking about the playground, his back pocket bulging meaningfully, just the trace of top string showing, Farkas was a continual, walking, living, surly challenge.

As a marble player, he had long since been barred from civilized games. His persistent use of blue-steel ball bearings, lightly polished with 3-In-One Oil, had reduced our heisty and spitsie games to a shambles, leaving the playground strewn with the wreckage of shattered comsies, precious aggies—and blasted hopes. Farkas played for keeps, in the truest sense of the word. An aggie belted by one of Farkas' cannonballs ceased to exist, dissolving in a quick puff of pulverized ash.

Farkas' secret was not in his choice of weapons alone. He had the evil eye. We all have seen this eye at one time or another in our lives, glimpsed fleetingly, perhaps, for a terrifying, paralyzing moment on the subway, among a jostling throng on the sidewalk in the midst of a riotous Saturday night, peering from the gloom through the bars of a deathhouse cell in a B movie at the Orpheum, or through the steamy, aromatic air of the reptile house. It is not easy to describe the effect that Farkas' eye had on the playground of the Warren G. Harding School. I know that such a thing is anatomically not possible, but Farkas' eye seemed to be of the purest silver-gray, totally unblinking and glowing from within with a kind of gemlike hardness. These eyes, set in his narrow, high-cheekboned weasel face above a sharp, runny nose, have scarred forever the tender psyches of countless preadolescents. Many's the kid who awakened screaming, drenched with cold sweat in the dead of night, dreaming wild nightmares of being chased over fences, under porches, through garages by that remorseless weasel face. The closest thing I have ever seen to the general quality, both physical and spiritual, of Scut Farkas was when, on a sunny afternoon on a Florida dock, I came face to face with a not-quite-deceased, eight-foot mako shark. Scut Farkas, at ten, was a man not to be trifled with.

He was the only kid I had ever heard of who rarely smoked cigars, cigarettes or corn silk. Farkas chewed apple-cured Red Mule Cut Plug. In class and out. As a spitter, Farkas unquestionably stands among the all-time greats. During class he generally used his inkwell as a target, while on the playground he usually preferred someone else's hair. Few dared to protest, and those who did lived to regret it. Farkas' glance boring gun-hard across the classroom carried a message to every male in the class, save one, at one time or another. It read: "I'll get you after school." The kid, knowing he was doomed, often wet his pants right there and then.

He had never been known to refer to *any* of his classmates by other than their last name only. The use of the first name somehow would have been a sign of camaraderie or weakness, and would have undermined his position as an unbending belligerent. The victim's last name was always followed by the same phrase: "Ya chicken bastard!"

His only known rival in pure thuggishness was the equally infamous Grover Dill. The two had formed an unspoken alliance, each recognizing the other as extremely dangerous—an alliance that held the rest of the kids in total subjugation.

As a competitive top spinner, Farkas was universally recognized as unbeatable. The combination of Mariah and Farkas' short, whistling three-quarter-lash movement was devastating. He sacrificed accuracy for sheer power, like a fast-ball pitcher with a streak of wildness. When Mariah hit, there was no return.

Occasionally a challenger, getting wind of Farkas' over-powering reputation at Warren G. Harding, would show up at recess from some foreign school. A ripple of excite-ment would move quickly through the motley throng as the two battlers squared off. There was a strong streak of chauvinism among the Warren G. Harding students. It could be said that we felt, "Warren G. Harding, right or wrong"—except when Scut Farkas was facing down a challenger from, say, St. Peter's parochial school, or George Rogers Clark. Farkas did not carry the colors of Warren G. Harding on his back. Like all true outlaws, the only color he recognized was blood-red. The other guy's, of course.

Week after week, month after month, we stood by helplessly as Scut Farkas and Mariah made wreckage of the best tops in Hohman, Indiana. Not only that; we were forced by a single scythelike sweep of his evil eye to applaud his victories. This was the unkindest cut of all. I remember the hated words rattling in my throat as I banged Flick on the back: "Old Farkas sure did it." Flick hollowly answering: ". . . Yeah."

Pocketing Mariah and hawking fiercely, Farkas would swagger sideways into the gloom of the boys' bathroom to look for somebody to hit. Another notch was added to his already well-notched belt.

This was the nature of my enemy as I practiced day after day in the basement next to the furnace, perfecting, honing, polishing my burgeoning technique. Why I did it, I cannot tell. Some men are driven to climb Everest, others to go over Niagara Falls in barrels or beach balls. Some are driven to wrestle crocodiles barehanded. I only knew that in the end there would be just Farkas and me, and our tops.

One thing was sure: To get hold of a top that could even stay in the same ring with Mariah, I would have to do better than the measly assortment that Old Man Pulaski kept in the candy case among the jawbreakers, the JuJu Babies and the wax teeth. Pulaski's tops were not fighting tops. They were little-kid playing-around tops; weak, defenseless, wobbly, minnowlike, they were even used by girls.

"Do you have any other tops but them little ones?"

"D'ya wanna top or don'tcha?" Old Man Pulaski glared down at me from behind his bloody butcher's apron while the jostling knot of Lithuanian and Polish housewives clamored for soup bones.

"Yeah, but I got that kind."

"Here, how 'bout a nice red one?" He reached into the case, trying to hurry the sale.

"Ya got any black ones?"

"Aw, for Chrissake, black tops! Come on, kid, I ain't got no time to fool around!"

"Scut Farkas got one."

"I told Scut Farkas if he ever came in again I'd kick his behind. He didn't get no black top here."

"Well, he's got one."

"Ask *him* where he got it." He roared off back to the meat counter.

Obviously, that was out of the question. Asking Farkas where he got Mariah was about like asking King Kong where he got his fangs. So I began methodically to visit candy store, dime store, toy store—any kind of store where they might conceivably have tops. Every day on my paper route I sniffed and hunted. From time to time I even bought what looked like a promising challenger, but I knew deep down in my heart that none of them came close to Mariah. Some were better than Pulaski's, some worse. I even discovered all sorts of tricky, effete, frilly tops I had never before seen or heard of. This went on well through spring. Then, late one balmy day, slowly pedaling home on my Elgin bicycle—the pride of my life—its foxtails hanging limply in the soft air, my mind a good five light-years away, I came unexpectedly to the end of my search.

I was at least four miles beyond my usual range, in a run-down, rickety tenement section of town, near the roundhouse. The steady crash and roar of switch engines,

the shrieking and booming of Monon freight cars went
on 24 hours a day, seven days a week in this country.
Even when the sun was out brightly, the skies here were
gray. I rarely got over this far. It was foreign territory.
I pedaled aimlessly along the dingy, dark street, the
curbs lined with elderly, disreputable automobiles, reading signs as I went. For the first few years after you
really learn to read, you read everything in sight carefully.

BEECH-NUT TOBACCO . . . BULL DURHAM . . . FISK TIRES
. . . ROOM FOR RENT—RAILROADERS WELCOME . . .
COMMIT NO NUISANCE . . . CHILI PARLOR, HOT TAMALES
. . . SHOESHINE . . . BARBERSHOP . . . SNOOKER TABLES
. . . TOTAL VICTORY NEWSSTAND AND NOTIONS . . .
LUMP COAL . . .

Wait a minute. TOTAL VICTORY NEWSSTAND AND NOTIONS.
It was a tiny, dark sliver of a shop, wedged in between
two gloomy red-brick buildings, about the size of those
places where a man sells celluloid combs and hunches
over a lathe making keys. I swung over to the curb,
squeaked on the brakes and dropped the bike in back
of a derelict Hudson Terraplane. In front of the Total
Victory, a faded-red-metal slotted newspaper display case
leaned against a locked Coca-Cola icebox. The window
of the store was impenetrable by human gaze, covered
with a rich, dank patina of locomotive smoke, blast-furnace dust and the fine essence of Sinclair Oil from the
nearby refineries. Faded posters hawking Copenhagen

Snuff, Sweet Orr work gloves and Lava Soap, the mechanic's friend, completed the job. For a second or two, once inside, I couldn't see a thing, it was so dark and dingy.

"What d'ya want, sonny?" I peered around the high glass case containing stacks of snuffboxes and tablets, looking for the speaker.

"What d'ya want?" An ancient lady wearing a black shawl over her head, the way most Polish ladies did in our neighborhood, stared piercingly at me.

"Uh . . ."

"D'ya want some orange pop, sonny?" She spoke with the slightest trace of a European accent.

"You got any tops?"

"Why, yes, sonny."

She disappeared behind the counter for a long moment. The shop's air was heavy with the scent of cabbage, garlic, tobacco juice and old clothes. Outside, a diesel engine blatted its horn thunderingly, rumbling off into the middle distance.

"How about these, sonny?"

She hoisted a cardboard box of tops onto the counter. I might have known it. She must have got these tops from the same place Pulaski got his—weak-kneed trifles that you saw everywhere.

"Uh . . . is that all you got?"

"How 'bout a red one, sonny?"

"Uh . . . you got any other kind?"

"Other kind? These are good tops, sonny."

"Naw, I got one a them. 'Bye."

I started to leave, as I had done so many times in the past, from every dinky candy store in town. Just as I got to the door:

"Hey, sonny, come back here."

Vaguely uneasy, I turned, one foot out on the sidewalk, the other on the greasy floor, my Keds ready to spring for the Elgin. She had disappeared into the back of the store behind a beaded curtain. She re-emerged into the murky gloom, carrying a cardboard Quaker Oats box. She set it down on the counter and began fishing in it with a withered claw. I waited, figuring she was going to spring a yo-yo on me, a toy for boobs and idiots, a sop for the untalented.

She pulled out a tangled mass of rubber bands, string, a couple of old clothespins and what looked like a dead mouse. A switch engine breathed asthmatically in the ambient air outside—followed by muffled curses from the brakemen.

"Aha! Here she is!" She fished scratchingly, unable to grab whatever it was.

"I wouldn't sell this top to everybody, sonny."

"Yeah?" I was ready to jump.

"But I can tell you need a top, sonny." She cackled, her faint white beard glinting dully. Her hand snaked out of the can, clutching something round.

Great Scott! Cradled in her talons lay a malevolent duplicate of Scut Farkas' evil Mariah. A duplicate in everything—spirit, conformation, size, everything—except color. It was a dull, burnished, scuffed silvery-pewter, a color I had never seen on a top before. But then, except for Mariah, I had never seen a black one, either.

"It's been used, so it won't cost you much, sonny."

"How much?" I was almost afraid to ask.

"I'd say ten cents, sonny. It's imported. She's a Gypsy top."

I was In. It was one of those few moments when I was well-heeled, carrying a full 12 cents in my jeans. I forked over my two nickels as calmly as I could and took possession of what was to prove to be a historic find. I had at last come together with the greatest fighting top I had ever seen. It had an oily, heavy, solid feel, a nice comfortable heft like, say, a Colt snub .38 Special feels to the hand. I had already decided to call it Wolf.

"Good luck, sonny. Careful, she's a mean one."

Outside, the switchyard mumbled and muttered as a long, clanking string of flat beds rumbled toward the steel mill. With Wolf safely in my hip pocket, I pedaled furiously through the twilight toward Cleveland Street. The showdown had begun. I knew it. And somewhere in his lair, Scut Farkas must have known it, too.

That night after supper, under a dim yellow light bulb in the basement, next to the looming furnace that dominated the underworld below our house, I carefully wound my best top string around Wolf for the first time, pulling each loop hard and tight so that it lay flat against the preceding one, until finally Wolf was cocked and ready for action.

The string itself is highly important to a genuine expert. I preferred the hard, green, twisted cord that knotted solidly and got a good bite on the side of the top. This type of string was not easy to use, but once the technique was mastered, nothing could come near it. I had long since outgrown the standard wooden button for the end of the string, using instead a thin, one-inch mother-of-pearl button stolen from my mother's sewing basket. There were three extras stashed away in my dresser drawer for emergencies.

As the dim bulb illuminated a faint circle on the gray concrete floor, I scratched out a mark in the exact center of the pool of light for a target and stepped back into almost full darkness. I could smell the moldering old tires that my father kept hanging on the walls just in case someday he might pick up another Hupmobile, and the mildewed Sunday papers of years back that lay piled against the concrete-block walls, and the scent of countless generations of field mice who had lived out their lives in this basement, and the dusty Mason jars filled with grape jelly and strawberry preserves that lined the plank shelves under the steps, and the sharp rubber smell —bitter and strong—of the coiled garden hose under the workbench, and the more subtle but pervasive aroma of a half ton of damp soft coal in the pitchblack bin, all held together with the soapy dankness of the drains, covered with perforated iron lids, that every week carried the family's used wash water back into Lake Michigan.

Deliberately and meticulously, I set Wolf down on the concrete floor for the first time. We were made for each other, just the way Mariah was made for Scut. The personality of tops is an odd thing. Mariah spun with an angry ferocity, a carnivorous drive that was despised and feared by everyone who had the bad luck to see it in action. Wolf, on the other hand, was steadier, giving off a note higher in pitch than Mariah but in some ways even more deadly. Mariah was a hot-blooded animal; Wolf, cold-blooded, snakelike. It would be an interesting meeting.

Again I laid the top precisely on the mark I had made, getting the feel of it, gradually letting myself out, feeling the full flush of rising excitement and mounting confidence as I gradually mastered the sinister Wolf. Even from the start, however, I had the sneaky, uneasy feeling that somehow I didn't really *own* this top. At first I felt that it was just because I was not used to it, little suspecting how right I was.

For two weeks, every night, Wolf and I practiced together in the basement. I had decided not to show him to anyone until we could take on Farkas. No telling what might have happened if Farkas had heard of the existence of Wolf, and my plans, before I was ready to really give him a battle. Even at that, I knew very well that my chances of breaking even with Farkas, let alone defeating him, were as slim as the chances of that proverbial snowball in hell.

In public I began throwing my weight around with second-string tops, until the word slowly began to spread throughout the gym, the auditorium, the homerooms; till at recess time I could always draw a small claque of fans goading me on to belt some poor kid's top into the boondocks.

Since the day Farkas had publicly humiliated me, he no longer even deigned to note my topwork. Once, however, he paused briefly, while twisting Jack Robertson's arm behind him and belting him in the ribs with his free hand, to spit a thin spray of tobacco juice over my orange top, which had just landed neatly beside Delbert Bumpus' yellow ball-bearing spinner. He might have taken me on right then and there, but he was busy giving Robertson his refresher course. Periodically, Farkas treated every kid in the class to a good, brisk, tendon-snapping arm twist. He shoved the victim's wrist up between his shoulder blades, pushing up and twisting out, until the supplicant's face turned ashen, his eyes bugged out and his tongue lolled in agony, Farkas yelling: "C'mon, you son of a bitch. Say it!"

". . . Graaahhhkkk!"

"C'mon, say it! You son of a bitch." Farkas gives him two more degrees of twist and brings his knee smartly into contact with the tailbone of the sufferer.

"I said SAY it!"

The victim, looking piteously at the ring of silent, scornful watchers, including, no doubt, his ex-girlfriend, finally squeaked out: "I'm a chicken bastard."

"Say it again, louder."

"I'M A CHICKEN BASTARD!" With that, Farkas hurled the pain-wracked body violently into the stickers.

"Gimme a cigarette, Dill."

And the two of them would go skulking off toward the poolroom. He gave this refresher course about every six months, to all of us. We figure he kept a list and checked us off when our time came.

It was Friday. I knew that today would be the day. Somehow you know those things. It had rained all night, a hard, driving, Midwestern drenching downpour. Now, as I toyed with my Wheaties, I could feel the edge of danger mounting within me.

"Will you listen to me? I'm talking to you."

"Ah . . . what?"

"When I'm talking to you, I want you to listen. You sit there like you've got potatoes in your ears!"

My mother always had a thing about my not listening; also dragging my feet. That drove her crazy. She always yelled that I didn't walk straight, either.

"How many times have I told you not to slump like that while you're eating? It isn't good for your stomach."

I scrunched around in my chair, pretending I was listening to her.

"You'd better be home early this afternoon, because you've got to go to the store. I don't want to have to tell you again."

"Yeah, yeah."

"How many times have I told you not to say 'Yeah'?"

". . . Yeah."

This went on for about three hours or so, until I finally got out of the house, with Wolf stuck down deep in my hip pocket, with two other, lesser, tops in my front right-side pocket. I was loaded for bear.

It looked like rain as I walked through the alleys, over the fences, through the vacant lots on my way to the playground, kicking sheets of water up from muddy puddles, skipping bottle caps into new lakes as I moved toward the battlefield. A few other kids drifted in the same direction from the next block. The trees dripped warm water under the low, gray, ragged clouds. Off to the north, toward Lake Michigan, even though it was full daytime, the steel mills glowed dark red against the low-hanging overcast.

At last on the playground, I began my carefully thought-out scheme. "Hey, Kissel, how 'bout a little action?"

My top, the second-string orange one, whistled out and landed with a click on the asphalt.

"How 'bout it, Kissel?"

I scooped up the top, this time laying her down on one of the school steps, making it walk downstairs a step at a time, a neat trick from my basic repertoire. Finally goaded, Kissel pulled out of his pocket his lumpy little green top.

"I won't split it. Just nick it a little, Kissel. Don't worry."

A few onlookers had drifted into range, sensing something important afoot. I was deliberately overplaying my hand.

"I'll even let you go first, Kissel. Come on—chicken?" I spun my top temptingly in front of Kissel's Indian Tread tennis shoes. He couldn't resist any longer. He bit hard.

"All right, smart guy," he said, "take that!" His green top narrowly missed mine, bouncing on the asphalt and then settling down into its pedestrian buzz. Quickly I scooped up my top, wound it up and let him have it. His green toy careened drunkenly into the gutter.

"Sorry, Kissel. I just can't control it." I put my top back into my pocket, saying loudly:

"There's no good top men around here, anyway. Let's get up a game of softball."

I had made sure that before any of this happened, Grover Dill was in the throng. I knew only one thing could happen after such an outrageous remark. Even now his sloping shoulders, his thick neck, his ragged crewcut were disappearing in the direction of the alley behind the school where he and Farkas smoked cigars, chewed tobacco, hatched plots and went over their refresher-course check lists. I must admit that I felt no little nervousness at this point, but it was too late to turn back. The die was cast.

Nervously I fished a Tootsie Roll out of my pocket, and chewed furiously to cover up. Sure enough, not five minutes had passed—in fact, we were in the middle of choosing up sides for the softball game—when a tremendous wallop from behind sent me sprawling into a puddle. Instantly the mob surged forward. Looking up from the mud, I saw Farkas holding Mariah casually in his left hand, while spinning his greasy black top string like a lariat in his right. It whistled faintly.

"Get up, ya chicken bastard."

He quickly wound the string around Mariah and flicked it high into the air, catching it on his palm as it came down. She spun efficiently on his hand for a moment before he closed his talons over her.

"Come on, get up."

Slowly I arose, pretending to be contrite.

"What's the matter, Farkas? What did I do? Gee whiz!" A low snicker went through the multitude. They recognized the signs, the old familiar signs. To a man, they had uttered those words themselves from time to time. They enjoyed seeing others in the trap.

"Get out ya top."

"My *top?*"

"GET IT OUT!"

A few drops of rain had begun to fall, and it seemed to grow darker by the second. By now the crowd had grown, until we were ringed by a motley circle of noncommittal faces. Every kid on the playground was in the crowd. The word was out. Farkas was getting someone, and Farkas demanded an audience. Nervously, I pulled out my poor doomed orange top. There was no hope for it once Farkas zeroed in his sights. I had carefully planned this sacrifice.

"We'll flip for firsties," Farkas barked, his eyes cold, Mariah resting at the ready.

"Flip, Dill. Heads."

His crony spun his famous two-headed nickel into the gray air.

"Heads. You win, Scut," Dill snarled in my direction.

The crowd murmured ominously, but stilled instantly when Farkas glanced quickly around to spot who the wise guys were.

"Spin, jerk."

I wound my orange top tightly, dug my feet as hard as I could down on the asphalt. Using my underhand sweep, fast and low, I laid her down a good 15 feet away.

Farkas half crouched, Mariah digging into his grimy thumb, the rusty metal washer he used for a button jabbing out between his fingers. His arm jerked down and out, the string snapped, black Mariah struck. That is, she missed, by less than an inch. The two tops spun side by side for a moment until I darted forward, scooped mine up and backed off. Before me, black Mariah sat toadlike, growling moodily, while Farkas watched with ill-concealed contempt.

I decided to go in for the kill. Again my arm dropped, the orange top streaked out, heading straight for black Mariah's vitals. It was a good shot. Farkas knew it. He snarled low in his throat. The crowd murmured excitedly as my orange top cracked smartly against Mariah—but wobbled off weakly among the feet of the onlookers. Mariah did not budge.

"Spin it again, ya chicken bastard."

Farkas picked up Mariah and waited for my next move. I knew this was it. I had missed my chance. But then, I wasn't counting on this poor top. My big move was on the way.

I spun. Then, with his accustomed sardonic ease, the showboat attitude he always displayed when picking up a scalp, Farkas neatly cracked my top into kingdom come, the deadly spike sending up a thin spray from the wet pavement.

By habit or tradition, the multitude indicated its approval of Scut's victory:

"Wow!"

"Holy smokes!"

"Gee whiz!"

"Whoooiee!"

And other sickening sounds.

Farkas casually picked up Mariah, turned his back on me and, followed by Dill, started to walk away, the crowd parting before them. It was *now!*

My hand whipped down into my back pocket, quickly snaked Wolf out into the open, and in the twinkling of a moment, I had him wound and instantly laid Wolf down hard and solid. Its high, thin note, steady as a dentist's drill and twice as nasty, cut through the falling rain and stopped Farkas in his tracks. He turned and stared for a long instant. His eyes seemed to widen and he actually, for a moment at least, appeared to grow pale—but even more baleful—as he recognized Wolf for what it was. Between us, the silver-gray top sang tauntingly. I didn't say a word. Wolf said it all.

The crowd, sensing that something had happened, became hushed and tense. Somewhere off in the south a mutter of thunder rumbled and stilled. Casually, Farkas wound his top string about Mariah and, without a word, laid it down with a hard, vicious, overhand, cracking shot that missed Wolf by the thickness of a coat of paint. The two tops spun together with no daylight between,

Mariah's bass rumble blending with the shuddering whine of Wolf in an eerie, angry duet.

Quickly I picked up Wolf, and this time, with all the force I had, I went in for the big one. A silver-gray streak, Wolf blurred out before me. The crowd gasped audibly. Scut peered sharply down at Mariah as Wolf screamed toward the *coup de grâce*.

I couldn't believe it! Moving like a shadow over Mariah, Wolf missed by the thickness of a hair. Instantly, with a cackle, Farkas gathered in Mariah and, with a guttural laugh, sent her down the rails to finish off Wolf. I had seen him really angry at an opponent before, but nothing like this. I was afraid to look, half turning away—but the roar of the crowd told me that, incredibly, Mariah had missed!

It was my turn now. For once in my life, my nerves were like steel. This time, with infinite deliberation, I aimed and carefully let fly, a little higher, with more lift, a more deadly trajectory. Wolf rose and came down like a fiend of hell, swooping out of the sky like some gray eagle. But at the last impossible instant, it actually seemed to change course in mid-air, grazing Mariah slightly and skittering off into a puddle.

Again and again we attacked each other, first Wolf, then Mariah. Over and over we drove at each other's vitals. Something was happening that slowly began to dawn first on Farkas and me and then on the crowd. Incredibly, these two tops seemed to be *afraid* of each other. Either that, or they were somehow, in some way, mysteriously jinxed.

My arm ached. Farkas paused only to blow his nose on his sleeve before going back to the attack. It was growing darker; and it became obvious to us that at this rate, neither of us was going to scalp the other. The two insane tops, grimy, covered with mud, leaped like live things—ricocheting, leapfrogging, hovering over each other, behaving in a way that no top before or since has ever acted. They hated each other; yet they seemed to be in league.

Dill, like all good toadies, tried everything he could to snaffle Wolf, kicking up mud when I spun, going even to the extent of nudging me violently on two occasions, hoping to tip the balance. Farkas was game but growing angrier and fiercer by the second, until finally he grabbed Mariah up from the scratched and scarred battlefield, looked at me with a long, searing gaze of hate and finally said, in a low boice:

"OK, ya chicken bastard. Let's play keepers."

Keepers meant that one kid would own *both* these tops, if his top could drive the other out of a circle made on the concrete with chalk. It was the final test of topping. Farkas was gambling Mariah against Wolf. Dill quickly drew a lopsided circle on the concrete sidewalk that paralleled the asphalt. The hard surface was perfect for keepers.

"You go first," Farkas commanded.

Under the rules of the game, you were not allowed to strike your opponent's top directly, so it really didn't matter who went first. The tops themselves fought it out, walking each other around the circle until one or the other was pushed out.

I spun Wolf—little realizing for the last time. It whistled out in a low arc, landing fair in the center of the circle. I put as much power on the spin itself as I could, cracking the string with a hard, flat snap. Wolf spun, waiting for Mariah, its spike ringing sharp and hard. Farkas spun Mariah, and the two tops hummed within an inch of each other. Slowly they walked, closer and closer, as the crowd closed in. Closer and even closer, then finally— tick . . . tick . . . tick—they touched. Locked in mortal combat, first Wolf and then Mariah, then Mariah and then Wolf, ticking, humming in rising and falling cadence as they edged toward the dreaded line. Which would go out first?

For a few moments it seemed as though Wolf was doomed, but then, righting itself, it shouldered Mariah closer. Impossibly, the two seemed to pick up speed as they spun. Angrier and angrier they grew, until suddenly, with a lunge, the two tops smashed together, both reeling in tandem in a mad, locked, spinning embrace *together* over the line and out of the circle. The rain, falling steadily, pattered down on the two hazy forms in the misty air.

Farkas, sensing victory, shouted: "YOURS IS OUT!"

He darted forward. The two tops continued to struggle and together they toppled over the curb, into the gutter, clicking, snarling crazily in the fast-running water, sending up sharp rooster tails of muddy foam. I moved as fast as I could to defend Wolf.

Suddenly, it was all over. The two tops, locked in mortal combat, disappeared down a sewer from which rose a deep roar of rushing water. They were gone. Never before had any of us seen tops behave like this!

Farkas, his face white, his eyes glazed, stared down into the raging flood through the grille of the drain. Then, without a word, he arose and, followed by Dill, walked off down the street in the rain. I knew I would never see Wolf again. But somehow I knew that neither Wolf nor Mariah were finished. They would go on. I don't know why I knew this, but I did, and I still do.

The crowd broke up into small knots. The great top days were over at Warren G. Harding School. A few weeks later, I rode over to the other side of town, looking for the Total Victory. One time, months later, I thought I saw it, but it turned out to be a place where they sold stuffed animals and rocking chairs. Off and on, for a while, I continued my search; but I never found it again.

"Gosh, I don't think we'll be able to leave for the lake today. My stomach. . . ." Instantly, a chorus of self-pitying moans and whimpers drowns out the hapless TV daddy. His TV wife, surrounded by her rosy-cheeked brood and a mountain of tennis rackets, suitcases, water skis and all the other paraphernalia for an on-the-go family holiday, reaches into her Mexican handbag, pulls out a blue bottle and hands it to him.

"Here, take two of these."

"Well, OK, but it's no use. I've tried everything."

Popping the pills into his mouth, he smacks his lips a couple of times and says irritably, "Why, these taste just like—*candy.*"

"There's no law that says medicine can't taste good," the family shouts in unison.

He swallows doubtfully, waits a moment for the little A's and B's to go to work, then breaks into a blinding

Ultra Brite smile. "Say, you're right. I feel *good* again."
Cheers.

"All right, then, let's get the show on the road," barks the TV momma, herding the happy family out the door toward the station wagon and vacationland.

My old man, I reflected gratefully as I snapped off the set, was not a TV daddy. For one thing, I have never heard one of them use anything like the language he employed in moments of stress. Had he been playing that same touching scene, it would have gone something like this:

Quick medium shot of a fifth-hand Olds in the family driveway. Close-up of the old man's face behind the wheel.

"HOLY CHRIST, I'M GONNA HEAVE! WHAT THE HELL WAS IN THAT RED CABBAGE?"

Quick pan to my mother, hair in curlers.

"What do you mean, red cabbage? Them seven beers. . . ."

Back to the old man, face now turning green.

"Forget that crummy trip!"

Sudden uproar from kids in back seat, including me. Quick cut to the old man.

"WHAT DID YOU SAY?"

Shot of his right hand sweeping the back seat like an avenging boom, knocking heads together indiscriminately. Pan to Mother:

"Here. Take a Tums."

Old man, bellowing:

"ARE YOU OUT OF YOUR MIND!"

Shot of door opening quickly, as he rushes into bushes. End of commercial.

That true-life vacation scene is all too reminiscent of the one we played out every year. The family took a vacation trip by car each and every time the earth completed its laborious cycle around the sun. It usually came in late July or the first two weeks in August, but it made no difference. It always went the same way. For 14 straight years, our vacations were spent in southern Michigan on the shores of colorful Clear Lake. Clear Lake—it was many things, but the one thing it wasn't was clear. In fact, it was never even clear why we went there, but we did. Such are the vacations of the humble.

From June on, five minutes after school let out, my kid brother and I were in a feverish sweat of anticipation about this annual pilgrimage. The old man, playing it cool, didn't get really heated up until maybe a month or so before the big day. My mother—who, incidentally, would never have made a TV momma—would begin laying in supplies. As far as I was concerned, the only thing that counted was my meager collection of dime-store fishing tackle and my BB gun. For weeks I gazed at fishhooks, rolled lead sinkers over my tongue, drenched my Sears, Roebuck 79-cent reel in 3-in-1 oil. To be honest, I don't think I could have made it as a TV kid. For one thing, there were the pimples; and for another thing, I had a tendency to smell in those days—as a result of a lot of time spent in alleys and under porches and crawling through bushes with Schwartz and Flick and Kissel and the motley collection of spotted dogs that always accompanied us wherever we went. Come to think of it, Schwartz and Flick and Kissel smelled, too; which may be why, to one another, none of us smelled. In any event, Right Guard was something we played, not something we squirted on ourselves.

About two weeks or so before the big day, the old man would take the Olds down to Paswinski's Garage for a tune-up, which in our case was purely a cabalistic ritual. It was like fingering a string of beads or burning incense. But southern Michigan was a long way from northern Indiana and the Olds was our only hope. She was a large, hulking four-door sedan of a peculiar faded green color that the old man always called "goat-vomit green." This was his big party joke. He always said it when everybody was eating. The Olds had been in the hands of at least four previous owners, all of whom had left their individuals marks on body and seat, fender and grille.

The week before vacation, the old man would go into high gear. On Monday of the last week, just after supper, he would make the Big Phone Call. Putting through a long-distance call to Michigan was not something that happened every day in our house.

"Is this long distance?" he shouted into the receiver. "Operator, I want to put through a long-distance call to Michigan." The rest of us sat in hushed excitement, trepidation and fear. This was crucial. Would there be a cabin available? The old man played it for all it was worth:

"Marcellus, Michigan. Ollie Hopnoodle's Feed and Grain Store. I wanna talk to Mr. Hopnoodle."

He listened intently, then put his hand over the phone and whispered:

"I can hear 'em ringing him! . . . Hello, Ollie? You old son of a bitch! Guess who this is. . . . Right! How did you guess? . . . We want the green one this year. . . . Yeah, the one on the other side of the outhouse. . . . You did? That's great!

"Ollie had two more holes put in the outhouse," he reported in an aside to us.

"OK, Ollie, see you next week."

The die was cast. We were on our way—almost. The week dragged by interminably—but finally it was Saturday night. All day, my mother had been cleaning up the house for the two-week hiatus, nailing down the screens, locking the basement windows, packing suitcases, trunks, cardboard boxes, laundry bags and wicker baskets with everything she could lay her hands on. The old man, who worked on Saturday, came roaring up the drive, the Olds already snarling in defiance over what was about to occur. He charged into the kitchen, his eyes rolling wildly, his very being radiating sparks of excitement.

"OK, now. This year we're all gonna get up early and we're gonna be on the road by six o'clock. No later! This time we're gonna beat the traffic!"

My mother, who had heard all this before, continued toiling stoically over her enormous pile of effluvia.

"When that alarm goes off at four-thirty," the old man said to no one in particular, "I don't want to hear no griping. OK, now, let's check the list."

Far into the night they went over every can of pork and

beans, every slice of bacon, every box of crackers, every undershirt and rubber band—even the jug of citronella, that foul, fetid liquid mystically (and erroneously) believed to be effective in warding off mosquitoes of the Michigan variety. Finally, sometime after midnight, the uproar slowly petered out.

A few minutes later, the alarm went off and my kid brother and I leaped out of the sack like shots. This was it! From the next bedroom came a muffled curse.

"Fer Chrissake, will ya shut that damn thing off!"

Mutterings from my mother as she put on her slippers in the dark.

"Don't worry," growled the old man in his familiar litany, "I'll get right up. I'm just resting."

More mutterings. "Look, I'm just resting my eyes! I'm getting right up!"

The vacation had begun as it always began. Already, not three minutes old and it was imperceptibly inching downhill. Five minutes later my mother, wearing her rump-sprung Chinese-red chenille bathrobe with tiny flecks of petrified egg on the lapels, her eyes puffed sleepily, peered down at a pot of simmering oatmeal in the clammy kitchen. Outside in the blackness, a few sparrows clinging to telephone wires chirped drowsily, pretending that they were real birds and not just sparrows living in a steel-mill town.

My kid brother and I ran insanely up and down the basement stairs, dragging stuff out of the coalbin that we figured we might need at the lake. For over a month I had been assiduously collecting night crawlers in a

Chase & Sanborn coffee can; I brought them up from the
basement to be ready to pack when the time came. I
toyed with my oatmeal, but it was such a great day that I
actually went ahead and ate it.

My brother, who had been known to go for over two
years without eating, was playing Pig in honor of the
festive occasion. This was a game invented by my mother
to euchre the little runt into eating. It consisted of my
mother saying:

"Randy, how does the little piggy go?"

His nostrils would flare, his neck would thicken, his
face, redden. He would grunt twice and look for approval
to my mother.

"Nice piggy. Here's your trough."

He would give another snort and then shovel his
snout deep into the red cabbage, mashed potatoes, oatmeal or whatever it was and slurp it up loudly. He
wasn't a TV kid, either. This morning, in excitement,
he polished off two troughs of Quaker Oats, usually his
quota for a month. My mother, her hair curlers clinking,
called out:

"Are you up?" Silence.

"Are you up?" Silence.

"It's getting late."

"SHUT UP, FER CHRISSAKE!"

Wearily, she bent back over the sink. She had been
this route before.

Half an hour later, the sun streaming in through the
kitchen windows finally flushed the old man out into
the open. By now, the mound of impedimenta filled the

kitchen and overflowed out onto the back porch. His B.V.D.s hanging limply, the old man weaved unsteadily between the piles and collapsed into a chair.

"Gimme some coffee."

He slumped unshaven, staring numbly at the kitchen table, until my mother set the coffee down in front of him. She did not speak. She knew that this was no time for conversation. He lit a Lucky, took a mighty drag and then sipped gingerly at the scalding black coffee, his eyes glaring malevolently ahead. My old man had begun every day of his life since the age of four with a Lucky and a cup of black coffee. He inhaled each one alternately, grimly, deeply. During this routine, it was sheer suicide to goad him.

The sun rose higher. And higher. It grew hotter and muggier, as only late July in northern Indiana can. The first faint whiff of oil-refinery smoke and blast-furnace dust eddied in through the screen door. Somewhere a cicada screamed into the brightening haze. Clotheslines drooped. My brother and I were busy carrying bags, suitcases and lumpy cardboard cartons tied with string out into the driveway. My mother wordlessly squeezed lemons for the lemonade we always carried along in our big two-gallon Thermos.

The old man stonily began his second cup. Halfway through it, he suddenly looked up, the sun now well over the high-tension wires and striking him full on his stubbled face.

"WELL!" he shouted. "ARE WE ALL SET TO GO?"

This was the signal that the *real* action could begin.

The old man was still alive for another day. It was vacationtime. He had been let out of the pen. My mother, picking up her cue, said:

"Well, everything's about set."

"OK, gimme that list."

He roared around the kitchen, his B.V.D.s flapping obscenely as he rechecked the pile of rubber ducks, beach balls, old inner tubes, spyglasses, straw hats, fielders' mitts —all of it. He rushed into the bathroom to shave and emerged a few minutes later with a wad of toilet paper plastered to a nasty gash on his chin. As I said, he was no TV daddy.

By now, we had moved perhaps a ton and a quarter of stuff out into the weeds of the back yard, which at this time of the year were usually knee high, filled with green caterpillars and millions of stickers. As always, Mrs. Kissel peered wistfully from her kitchen window next door. Since Mr. Kissel never worked, the Kissel family never took vacations.

The neighborhood dogs, sensing that something was afoot, scurried round and round the cardboard cartons, yipping. A couple of them did more than that. Piece by piece, carton by carton, every available inch of the back seat was packed solid. The old man had a Sears luggage rack clamped onto the roof of the Olds. The heavy stuff was loaded on top: comforters, folding camp chairs, beach umbrellas, his set of matched Montgomery Ward golf clubs—all piled high and held down with lengths of clothesline. Those wooden-handled, chrome-headed clubs represented his only foray into the magic world of the "Big People," as he called them, the ones who ran Chevy agencies and sauntered around the course on Sundays in checkered knickers.

At last he crawled in behind the wheel, rolled down his window and peered over a pile of junk next to him to see if my mother was in place. Back in the rear, my brother and I were wedged into two tiny cockpits burrowed into the wall of tightly packed essentials for living. My mother, for some reason, always pretended that going to Clear Lake was something like traveling to the North Pole. You had to be ready for anything. The doors were slammed, windows adjusted, and finally the old man gave his yearly cry:

"OK. Here we go!"

Outside in the yard, a motley collection of well-wishers had gathered, including Flick, Schwartz, Kissel and other smaller fry who moved in the substrata of kid life— nameless, noses running, never invited to play ball.

The old man turned the key in the dash and stepped on the starter. From deep within the bowels of the Olds- mobile came a faint click. He jabbed again at the starter. Another click. His neck reddened.

"Oh, fer Chrissake! That damn starter spring's stuck again!" The sun beat down mercilessly on our wheeled pyramid, the interior growing hotter by the second. En- raged, the old man threw the door open and rushed around to the front of the Olds, shouting:

"TURN THE KEY ON WHEN I JUMP UP AND DOWN ON THE BUMPER!"

He grabbed the radiator ornament, a shoddy copy of

the *Winged Victory*, climbed up on the bumper and began to bounce maniacally up and down. It was a routine we all knew well. The old man, his face beet red, the blood once again dripping from his gashed chin, hopped up and down in a frenzy. Once again, from deep within the Olds, came another faint click. Instantly, the old man shouted:

"DON'T NOBODY MOVE! SIT REAL STILL!"

He tore around the side of the car and eased himself into the driver's seat. It was a touchy moment. Carefully, so as not to create the slightest vibration, he pushed the starter button on the floor.

Gug gug gug gug. . . . It failed to catch.

The old man whispered hoarsely: "Don't nobody breathe."

He tried it again. G-gug gug . . . BBRRROOOOOOO-MMMM!

The mighty six-cylinder, low-compression Oldsmobile engine rattled into life, rocker arms clattering, valve springs clanging, pistons slapping. After all, 142,000 miles isn't exactly around the block. He threw her into reverse and slowly she lumbered backward down the driveway, swaying under the immense load of half the available stock of the A. & P.

Safely out on the street, he threw her into first. Painfully she began to roll forward. I peered out of the tiny crack of window available to me, a square of glass no more than three inches across, and saw my assembled friends standing dumbly along the sidewalk. For a brief instant, I felt a deep pang of regret about all the great things that were going to happen in the neighborhood while I was gone. From somewhere off to my left, amid the rumblings of the Olds, I heard the first muffled squeakings of my kid brother.

Two minutes later, we turned down a side road toward the main highway that wended its way listlessly past junk yards and onion patches toward the distant, rolling, sandy hills of Michigan. It was Sunday and already a solid line of automobiles, bumper to bumper, stretched from one horizon to the other, barely moving. The old man, his eyes narrowed with hatred, glared through the windshield at his most ancient and implacable foe —the traffic.

"Damn Sunday drivers! Stupid sons of bitches!"

He was warming up for the big scenes yet to come. As traffic fighters go, he was probably no more talented nor dedicated than most other men of his time. But what he lacked in finesse he more than made up for in sheer ferocity. His vast catalog of invective—learned in the field, so to speak, back of the stockyards on the South Side of Chicago—had enriched every Sunday-afternoon drive we ever took. Some men gain their education about life at their mother's knee, others by reading yellowed volumes of fiction. I nurtured and flowered in the back seat of the Olds, listening to my father.

At least we were on our way. No one could deny that. We crept along in the great line of Sunday traffic, the Olds muttering gloomily as its radiator temperature slowly mounted. My mother occasionally shouted back through the din in our direction:

"Are you kids all right?"

All right? I was out of my head with excitement. I looked forward to this moment all year long; it made Christmas and everything else pale to nothing. I had pored over every issue of *Field & Stream* in the barbershop, dreaming about tracking beavers and fording streams and making hunter's stew. Of course, nobody ever *did* any of those things in Michigan, but they were great to read about. One time, our scoutmaster took us out on a hike through Hohman and painted moss on the north side of all the fireplugs, so that we could blaze a trail to the vacant lot behind the Sherwin-Williams sign. But that was about the extent of my expertise in nature lore.

Hour after hour we inched northward, and finally burst out of the heavy traffic and turned onto the rolling, open highway that led through the sandy hills to Marcellus, Michigan. By now it was well along in the afternoon and the temperature inside the car hovered at maybe 15 or 20 degrees below the boiling point. The Olds had a habit of hitting a thrumming, resonant vibration at about 50 that jiggled the bones, loosened the molars, rattled the eyeballs and made all talk totally impossible. But over the roar, a faint squeak filtered through the cartons to my left. My mother turned in her seat, took one look and shouted at the old man to stop the car.

"WHAT THE HELL NOW?" he bellowed, as he pulled over to the side of the road under a pair of great, overhanging Michigan poplars. Everywhere around us the yellow-and-dun fields, mottled with patches of grapevines, stretched out to the horizon.

My mother dashed around the side of the car to my brother's door. I heard him being hauled out of his tiny capsule. Oatmeal, Ovaltine, caterpillars—everything he had downed in the past couple of days gushed out into the lilies.

I sat in my slot, peering out of the window at the alien landscape, my excitement now at fever pitch. Randy always got sick at about this point. That meant we were halfway there. Ashen-faced, he was stuffed back into his hole. Once again, the starter spring stuck. Once again, the old man raged up and down on the bumper. We were off.

It was then that the bombshell struck. Oh, no! OH, *NO!* I slumped deep down into the seat, a two-pound box of rice sliding from the shelf behind me and pouring its contents down the back of my neck. The Oldsmobile boomed on toward Clear Lake and its fighting three-ounce sunfish, its seven-inch bluegills and its five-inch perch, all waiting for me under lily pads, beside submerged logs and in the weed beds. *Oh, no!* I had left all my fishing tackle in the garage, all piled up next to the door, where I had taken it the night before to make sure I wouldn't forget it! Every sinker, every bobber, every hook I had saved for, polished, loved and cherished stood all neatly piled up back home in the garage.

"DAD!" I cried out in anguish. The great thrum of the Olds drowned me out.

"HEY, DAD!"

He glanced into the rearview mirror. "Yeah?"

"I LEFT ALL MY FISHING TACKLE IN THE GA-RAGE!" That meant *his*, too.

"WHAT?!" He straighted up in his sweat-soaked pongee shirt. "YOU DID WHAT?!"

"I . . . I. . . ."

"Oh, fer CHRIS*SAKE!* What next!" He spit through the open window into the onrushing hot air. It arced back into the rear window and missed my brother's head by an inch. My mother had been asleep now for some time. She never stirred through this disaster. Deep in my hole, I wept.

The steady, rumbling oscillation of the ancient Olds rolled back over me. Way down deep inside, the first faint gnawings of car sickness, like some tiny, gray, beady-eyed rat scurrying among my vitals, merged appropriately with the disappointment and the heat. A faint whiff of the sweetish-sour aroma of my kid brother filtered through the camp gear, drifted past my nose and out the window to my right. I stared with glazed eyes at the blur of telephone poles; at a barn with a huge Bull Durham sign on its side, with its slogan, HER HERO; at farmhouse after farmhouse; at a rusty tin sign with its faded message: HOOKED RUGS FOR SALE—ALSO EGGS.

The low hills, green, yellow and brown, wound on and on. I had wrecked the vacation. You might just as well tell Santa Claus to go to hell as leave your split-bamboo casting rod that you saved all year to buy and that had a cork handle and a level-wind Sears, Roebuck reel with a red jewel in the handle, and your Daredevil wiggler, so red and white and chromy, back in the garage amid the bald Goodyears and empty Simoniz cans. Oh, well, nothing ever works out, anyway. My little gray, furry rat reared on its hind legs, his fangs flashing in the darkness.

Over the steady hum of the mighty Olds engine I could hear the pitiful keening of my kid brother, who had now burrowed down to the floor boards in his travail. I stared sullenly out the window over a huge, rolled-up, dark-green comforter and an orange crate full of coffeepots and frying pans.

Suddenly: BA-LOOOMMMMPPP! K-tunk k-tunk kk-tunk k-tunk.

The car reeled drunkenly under the wrenching blows of a disintegrating Allstate tire. In the front seat, the driver wrestled with the heaving steering wheel. Overloaded by a quarter ton at least, the car continued to lurch forward.

Ding ding ding ding. It was down to the rim now. My father hauled back on the emergency brake. We slued up onto the gravel shoulder of the highway and rolled to a limping stop. He cut the ignition; but for a full 20 seconds or so, the motor continued to turn over, firing on sheer heat. Finally, she coughed twice and stopped. Dead silence enveloped us all. My father sat unmoving behind the wheel, his hands clenched on the controls in silent rage.

"Do you think it's a flat?" my mother chirped helpfully, her quick, mechanical mind analyzing the situation with deadly accuracy.

"No, I don't think it could be that. Probably we ran over a pebble." His voice was low, almost inaudible, drenched in sarcasm.

"I'm glad to hear that," she sighed with relief. "I thought for a minute we might have had a flat."

He stared out his window at the seared corn stalks across the road, watching the corn borers destroy what was left of the crops after the locusts had finished their work. We sat for possibly two minutes, frozen in time and space like flies in amber.

Then, in the lowest of all possible voices, he breathed toward the cornfield: "Balls."

Very quietly he opened the door, climbed out and stalked back to the trunk.

"ALL A' YA GET OUT!" he shouted.

My mother, realizing by this time that it hadn't been a pebble after all, whispered: "Now, don't get on his nerves. And don't whine."

The four of us gathered on the dusty gravel. Along the road behind us for a quarter mile at least, chunks of black, twisted rubber smoked in the sun and marked our trail of pain.

The old man silently opened the trunk, peered into the tangled mess of odds and ends that always filled it and began to rummage glumly among the shards. He removed the clamp that released the spare tire. In his world, spare tires were tires that had long since been given extreme unction but had somehow clung to a thread of life and perhaps a shred or two of rubber. Next, the jack.

We sat at a safe distance next to the cornfield, in the shade of an elm tree suffering from oak blight.

"Let's have a picnic while Daddy fixes the tire," suggested Mother cheerfully.

Daddy, his shirt drenched in sweat, tore his thumbnail off while trying to straighten out the jack handle, which was insanely jointed in four different spots, making it as pliable as a wet noodle and about as useful. While he cursed and bled, we opened the lunch basket and fished out the warm cream-cheese sandwiches and the lunch-meat-and-relish sandwiches.

"Gimme a peanut-butter-and-jelly sandwich," said my kid brother.

"We don't have peanut-butter-and-jelly."

"I want a peanut-butter-and-jelly sandwich."

"We have nice tuna and egg-salad sandwiches. On rye bread. You can pick the seeds out and have fun making believe they're little bugs."

"I WANT PEANUT-BUTTER-AND-JELLY!" Randy's voice was rising to a shrill pitch. Off in the middle distance, the jack clanked and rattled as the Olds teetered precariously on the flimsy metal support.

"GODDAMN IT! IN TWO SECONDS, I'M GONNA COME OVER AND BAT YOU ONE GOOD!" yelled the tire repairman.

Randy threw his tuna-salad sandwich out into the road, where it was instantly smashed flat by a Mack truck. Our little picnic went on. We drank lemonade, ate cookies.

Finally came the call: "OK. Pile in."

"How 'bout some music," my mother asked rhetorically as we rolled out onto the highway.

My father stonily drove on. Sometimes, after a particularly bad flat, he didn't speak to the family for upward of two weeks. I suspect that he always pictured heaven as a place where everybody was issued a full set of brand-new, four-ply U. S. Royal roadmasters, something he never in his life attained, at least on this earth.

My mother fiddled with the car radio, which hummed and crackled.

> *"Roll out the barrel*
> *We'll have a barrel of fun*
> *Roll out the barrel*
> *We've got the blues on the run. . . ."*

The Andrews Sisters were always rolling out barrels and having fun.

"Isn't that nice? Now, how 'bout playing a game, kids? What am I thinking of—animal, vegetable or mineral?"

We always played games in the car, like who could tell quicker what kind of car was coming toward us; or Count the Number of Cows; or Beaver, where the first guy who saw a red truck or a blue Chevy or a Coca-Cola sign could hit the other guy if he hollered "Beaver" first. Then there was Padiddle, which was generally played when there were girls in the car and had a complicated scoring system involving burned-out headlights, the highest point getter being a police car running

141

one-eyed. But Padiddle was never played in cars carrying mothers and kid brothers.

"*NOW* what the hell!" My father had broken his vow of silence.

Ahead, across the highway, stretched a procession of sawhorses with flashing lights and arrows and a sign, reading: ROAD UNDER CONSTRUCTION—DETOUR AHEAD 27.8 MILES.

Muttering obscenities, the old man veered to the right, onto a slanting gravel cow path. Giant bulldozers and road graders roared all around us.

"Holy God! This'll kill that spare!"

The Olds crashed into a hole. The springs bottomed. She bellowed forward, throwing gravel high into the air. The trail wound through a tiny hamlet—and then, a fork, where a red arrow pointed to the right: CONTINUE DETOUR. The road to the left was even narrower than the other, marked with a battered black-and-white tin sign perforated with rusting .22-caliber bullet holes: COUNTY ROAD 872 (ALTERNATE).

We fishtailed to a stop, yellow dust pouring in the windows.

"Gimme that map!"

The old man reached across the dashboard and snapped open the glove compartment just as a truck rumbled past, raining gravel onto the windshield and along the side of the car.

"What the hell is THIS?" He yanked his hand convulsively out of the glove compartment. It dripped a dark, viscous liquid.

"OK," he said with his best Edgar Kennedy slow burn. "Who stuck a Hershey bar in the glove compartment?" No one spoke.

"All right, who did it?" He licked his fingers disgustedly.

"What a goddamn mess!"

The mystery of the Hershey bar was the subject of bitter wrangling off and on for years afterward. I know that. I didn't stick it in there. If my brother had gotten hold of a Hershey bar, he would have eaten it instantly. It never did come out—but then, neither did the chocolate; forevermore, the Oldsmobile had a chocolate-lined glove compartment.

My father pored over the creased and greasy map. "Aha! Eight-seven-two. Here it is. It goes through East Jerusalem and hits four-three-eight. I'll tell you what. I'll bet we can beat this detour by crossing through four-three-eight to this one with the dotted red line, nine-seven-four. Then we'll cut back and hit the highway the other side of Niles."

Two and a half hours later, we were up to our hubs in a swamp. Overhead, four large crows circled angrily at the first disturbance their wilderness had seen in years. After backing and filling for half an hour, we finally managed to regain semisolid ground on the corduroy road that we had been thumping over for the past hour or so. None of us spoke. We long ago had learned not to say a word in times like these.

Our spattered, battered hulk hauled itself, at long last, back onto the main highway, after traveling over

143

patches of country that had not been seen by the eye of man since Indian times.

"I knew I'd beat the damn detour." When my father *really* loused up, he always tried to pretend it was not only deliberate but a lot of fun.

"Did you kids see those big crows? Weren't they big? And I bet you never saw quicksand before. That was really something, wasn't it?"

Leaving a trail of mud, we rumbled along smoothly for a few minutes on the blessed concrete.

"How 'bout some of those Mary Janes? Would you kids like some Mary Janes?" He was now in a great mood.

My mother scratched around in the luggage a few moments until she found a cellophane bag full of the dentist's delight. "Be careful how you chew 'em," she cautioned us futilely, "because if you're not, they'll pull your fillings out."

The sound of our munching was drowned out by the RRRAAAAWWWRRRR of a giant, block-long truck as it barreled past our struggling flivver, eclipsing us in a deep shadow. As the truck roared past, inches away, sucking the car into its slip stream, an overwhelming cacophony of sound engulfed us—a sea of insane squawks and cluckings.

"Chickens!" Randy hollered ecstatically.

Thousands of chickens peered at us through the windows on our left side. Stretching for a mile back of us, a wall of Leghorns was going by. Then they were past us and the mammoth truck pulled into the lane directly

144

ahead of us, shedding a stream of white feathers that struck the windshield and billowed around us and in the windows like a summer snowstorm. Almost immediately we were enveloped in a wrenching, fetid, kick-in-the-stomach stench; it swept over us in a tidal wave of nausea.

"When the swallows come back to Capistrano . . ." the Inkspots chimed in on the radio.

"Gaak! What a stink!!"

"Maybe you'd better pass him," suggested my mother through her handkerchief.

"Yeah. Here goes."

He floored the Olds, but nothing happened. She was already going her limit. Ahead, the driver of the chicken truck settled into the groove, a lumbering juggernaut rolling along at 55, spraying feathers and a dark-brown aroma over the countryside. Again and again, the old man edged out into the left lane, gamely trying to pass, but it was no use. The truck stayed tantalizingly just out of reach, the chickens squawking delightedly, their necks sticking out of the iron cages, their beady red eyes wild with excitement, as the driver happily headed to market. Occasionally, a stray egg whistled past or splashed into the radiator grille to join the dead butterflies, grasshoppers and dragonflies.

"I have to go to the toilet." Already we had stopped at 74 gas stations so that Randy could go to the toilet. His output was incredible.

"You'll just have to hold it."

It had begun to rain—big ripe summer drops. The

windshield wipers were stuck and now my father drove with his head craned out the window in order to see. Rain ricocheted off his face and splattered everything within a two-foot radius. It carried with it chicken feathers and other by-products that streamed back from the truck ahead. But this was not the first time we had been caught behind moving livestock. A load of ducks make chickens a pure joy. And one time we had been trapped for over four hours behind 37 sheep and at least 200 exuberantly ripe porkers on U.S. 41.

The rain suddenly stopped, just when the menagerie boomed into a turnoff, and peace reigned once again. A few feathers clung to the headlights here and there, but the last lingering aroma of the barnyard finally departed through the rear windows. Then:

"WAAAH! I GOTTA WEEWEE!"

"All *right!* But this is the last time, ya hear?"

No answer. Randy was promising nothing. Ahead, a one-pump gas station crouched amid the cornfields next to a white shack that had once been a diner but was now sinking into the clay, carrying with it its faded red sign with the single word EAT. Under a rusted soft-drink cooler sprawled a mangy hound, who greeted our arrival by opening one rheumy eye and lifting a leg to scratch wearily and indiscriminately at his undernourished room-and-boarders.

We pulled up next to the pump. A thin, creased, dusty old man wearing a blue work shirt and faded jeans sat chewing a toothpick beside the screen door on an old wooden chair, with his feet on a "Phillips 66" oil drum. He didn't stir.

"Fillerup, bub?"

"The kid's gotta go to the toilet."

He shifted the toothpick. "Round the side, past them tires."

"You can check the oil while we're waiting."

Taking one foot off the oil drum, then the other, the man struggled to his feet with painful deliberation, shuffled over to the car and fiddled with the hood latch for a minute or so. Finally getting the knack of it, he yanked it open, leaned over the engine, pulled out the dipstick and held it up. It dripped rich, viscous sludge onto the gravel.

"Needs about two and a half quarts." It *always* needed two and a half quarts. "You want the good stuff or the cheap stuff?"

"The cheap stuff. Put in the heaviest ya got." The old crate burned oil like a diesel.

My mother and Randy were back in the car now. It was a typical pit stop on our long caravan route to Clear Lake and paradise.

Doggedly, we swung back out onto the highway. Randy relieved, the Olds refreshed. A mile up the road, my mother, making conversation, said:

"Why didn't you get gas?"

"I didn't want any of that cheap bootleg gas that guy had. I'm waiting for a Texas Blue Station."

"The gauge says empty. Maybe you shoulda got some."

"That gauge is cockeyed. When it says empty, there's

over an eighth of a tank left. There oughta be a Texas Blue station ahead."

Texas Blue was an obscure gasoline that had at one time sponsored the Chicago White Sox ball games on radio, thereby winning my father's undying patronage. If Texas Blue backed the White Sox, it was *his* gas. He would have used it if they had distilled it from old cabbages.

Thirty seconds later, the car sputtered to a stop, bone dry. After sitting stony-faced for a long time behind the wheel, the old man silently opened the door, got out, slammed it, opened the trunk, took out the red can he always carried and continually used, slammed the lid shut and set out without a word for the gas station we had left a mile and a half behind. He plodded over the horizon and was gone.

We played animal, vegetable or mineral and drank more warm lemonade while we waited in the steamy heat. Forty minutes later he returned, his two gallon can filled to the brim with gas so cheap you could hear it knocking in the container. He smelled heavily of both gasoline and bourbon. He poured the former into the tank and shortly thereafter we once again entered the mainstream of humanity.

A single red sign stuck in the road's shoulder at a crazy angle whizzed by; in white letters, it read: LISTEN, BIRDS. My father lit another Lucky and leaned forward on the alert, peering through the bug-spattered windshield.

THESE SIGNS COST MONEY. The second red-and-white

announcement flashed by, followed quickly by the third: SO ROOST AWHILE.

The old man flicked his match out the side window, his neck craning in anticipation of the snapper. We drove on. And on. Had some crummy, rotten fiend stolen the punch line? Another sign loomed over the next hill. He squinted tensely.

GENUINE CHERRY CIDER FOR SALE.

"Fer Chrissake!" he muttered amid the thrumming uproar and the constant ping of kamikaze gnats and bettles on the spattered windshield. But finally it came, half hidden next to a gnarled oak tree at the far end of a long, sweeping curve: BUT DON'T GET FUNNY.

I didn't get it. But then, I didn't get much of anything in those days. A few yards farther on, the sponsor's name flashed by: BURMA-SHAVE. Up front, the old man cackled appreciatively; his favorite form of reading, next to the *Chicago Herald-American* sports section, was Burma Shave signs. He could recite them like a Shakespearean scholar quoting first folios. He had just added another gem to his repertoire. In the months to come, it would be referred to over and over, complete to location, time of day and pertinent weather information. In fact, he and his pal Zudock even invented their own Burma-Shave signs—pungent, unprintable and *single-entendre*. It would have been a great ad campaign, if the Burma-Shave company had the guts to do it.

It began to rain again. My father rolled up his window part way. Normally, the atmosphere in the Olds in full cry was a faint, barely discernible blue haze, an aromatic mixture of exhaust fumes from the split muffler, a whiff of manifold heat, burning oil, sizzling grease, dust from the floor boards, alcoholic steam from the radiator and the indescribably heady aroma of an antique tangerine, left over from last year's trip, that had rolled under the front seat and gotten wedged directly in front of the heater vent. Now subtly blended with this oleo were the heavenly scents of wet hay, tiger lilies, yellow clay and fermenting manure.

Ahead of us, a house trailer towed by a Dodge drifted from side to side as they, too, rumbled on toward two weeks away from it all. The old man muttered:

"Lousy Chicago drivers"—a litany he repeated over and over to himself, endlessly, while driving. It must have had the same sort of soothing effect on him that prayer wheels and mystic slogans had on others. He firmly believed that almost all accidents, directly or indirectly, were caused by Chicago drivers, and that if they could all be barred at birth from getting behind a wheel, cars could be made without bumpers and the insurance companies could turn their efforts into more constructive channels.

"Look at that nut!" The old man muttered to himself as the house trailer cut across the oncoming lane and rumbled out of sight up a gravel road, trailing a thick cloud of yellow dust.

My mother was now passing out Wrigley's Spearmint chewing gum. "This'll keep you from getting thirsty," she counseled sagely.

We were doing well, all things considered, having

stopped for Randy at only 75 gas stations so far. After licking off the sweet, dry coating of powdered sugar, I chewed the gum for a while and leafed restlessly through a Donald Duck Big Little Book that I'd brought along to pass the time; but I was too excited and kind of sick to worry about old Donald and Dewey and Huey and Louie.

Suddenly the front seat was in a great uproar. I sat up. My mother screamed and shrank away toward the door. The old man shouted above her shrieks:

"Fer Chrissake, it's only a *bee*. It's not gonna kill you!"

A big fat bumblebee zoomed over the pots and pans and groceries, banging from window to window as my mother, flailing her tattered copy of *True Romance,* cowered screaming on the floor boards next to the gearshift. The bee zoomed low over her, banked sharply upward and began walking calmly up the inside of the windshield, like he knew just what he was doing. Every year, a bee got in the car—the same bee. My mother had an insane fear of being stung. She had read in *Ripley's Believe It or Not!* that a bee sting had killed a man named Howard J. Detweiler in Canton, Ohio, and she never forgot it. The subject came up often around our house, especially in the summer, and my mother invariably quoted Ripley, who was universally recognized as an ultimate authority on everything. She screamed again.

"Goddamn it! Shut up! Do you want me to have an accident?" my father bellowed. He pulled off to the side of the road, flung his door open and began the chase.

"Gimme the rag outta the side pocket!" he yelled.

My mother, shielding her head with her magazine, interrupted her whimpering long enough to shriek: "Where is he? I can hear him!"

The bee strolled casually up the windshield a few inches farther, humming cheerfully to himself. The old man tore around to the other side of the car to get the rag himself. Sensing that he had made his point, the bee revved his motors with a loud buzz and was out the window. He disappeared back down the road into the lowering skies of early evening, obviously getting set for the next Indiana car to show up over the hill.

"He got away, the bastard!" My father slid back into his seat, threw the Olds into gear and pulled back out onto the asphalt.

"OK, he's gone. You can get up now." His voice dripped with scorn.

My mother crawled back up into her seat, flushed and shaking slightly, and said in a weak voice: "You never can tell about bees. I read once where. . . ."

My father snorted in derision: "Howard J. Detweiler! I'd like to know where that goddamn bee stung him that it killed him. I'll bet I know where it got him!" he roared.

"Shhhh. The kids are listening."

"Hey, look! There's Crystal Lake." My father pointed off to the left.

I sat bolt upright. Way off past a big gray farmhouse and a bank of black trees under the darkening sky was a tiny flash of water.

A gravel road slanted off into the trees, bracketed by a thicket of signs: BOATS FOR RENT BATHING FISHING OVERNIGHT CABINS BEER EATS. We were in vacationland.

Oh, boy! In the back seat, I had broken out into a frenzied sweat. In just a few minutes, we would be there at that one-and-only place where everything happened: Clear Lake! For months, when the snow piled high around the garage and the arctic wind whistled past the blast furnaces, into the open hearth and around the back porch, under the eaves and through the cracks in the window sills, I had lain tossing on my solitary pallet and dreaming of Clear Lake, imagining myself flexing my magnificent split-bamboo casting rod, drifting toward the lily pads, where a huge bronzeback—an evil, legendary smallmouthed bass named Old Jake—waited to meet his doom at my hands.

I would see myself showing my dad how to tie a royal-coachman fly, which I had read about in *Sports Afield*. He would gasp in astonishment. I also astounded my mother in these dreams by demonstrating an encyclopedic grasp of camp cookery. I had practically memorized an article entitled "How to Prepare the Larger Game Fish." The text began: "A skillful angler knows how to broil landlocked salmon and lake trout in the 25-to-40-pound weight range. . . ." I had never *seen*, let alone cooked, a salmon or a trout or a pike or anything else—except for little sunfish, perch, bullheads and the wily crappie—but I was ready for them.

We rounded a familiar curve and rolled past a green cemetery dotted with drooping American flags. Steaming, the Olds slowed to a crawl as we inched past the general store, with a cluster of yellow cane poles leaning against its wooden front amid a pile of zinc washtubs. We had arrived.

"Now, look, you kids stay in the car. HEY, OLLIE!" the old man shouted out of the side window toward the feed store. "HEY, OLLIE, WE'RE HERE!"

Through the rain-spattered windshield, we could see that a few lights were on here and there in the ramshackle white-clapboard buildings overhung with willows and sweeping elm trees that lined the street. A tall figure in overalls strolled across the sidewalk and plunked his size-14 clodhopper on the running board, battered farmer's straw hat pushed to the back of his head.

"By God, ya made it." His Adam's apple, the size of a baseball, bobbed up and down his skinny neck like a yo-yo.

"Yep. We're here, Ollie."

"How was the trip?"

"Pretty good. Got a bee in the car, though."

"Back just before ya hit Crystal Lake?"

"That's right."

"Just before ya come to Henshaw's barn?"

"Yep."

"Gol durn. That son of a gun's been doin' that all summer. Got me twice."

Ollie owned six cabins on the shore of Clear Lake, which was rimmed solidly with a thick incrustation of summer shacks—except at the north end, where the lake was swampy and the mosquitoes swarmed.

"I saved the green one for you. She's all set. I emptied out the boat this morning."

A jolting shot of excitement ripped through me. The boat! *Our* boat, which I would row and anchor and bail out, and hang onto and cast my split-bamboo rod— My split-bamboo rod! I had forgotten for hours that I had left it all back in the garage.

"How's the fishing this year?" asked the old man.

"Well, now, it's a funny thing you asked. They sure were hittin' up to about a week or ten day ago. Guy from Mishawaka stayin' in cabin three got his limit a' walleye every day. But they slacked off 'bout a week ago. Ain't hittin' now."

"I guess I shoulda been here last week." It was always "last week" at Clear Lake.

"They might hit crickets. I got some for sale."

"I'll be over in the morning to pick some up, Ollie. I got a feeling we're gonna hit 'em big this year." The old man never gave up.

We turned off the main highway and drove along the beloved, twisting dirt road—now a river of mud—that led through cornfields and meadows, down toward the magical lake.

"Ollie looks skinnier," my mother said.

"He's just got new overalls," my father answered, sluing the Olds around a sharp bend. Night was coming on fast as it does in the Michigan lake country, black and chill. The rain had picked up. In the back seat, I was practically unconscious with excitement as the first cot-

155

tages hove into view. Between them and the trees that ringed them was the dark, slate void of the lake.

"She looks high," my father said. He always pretended to be an expert on everything, including lakes. Already my mother was plucking at pickle jars, Brillo pads, clothespins, rolls of toilet paper and other drifting odds and ends of stuff that she had banked around her in the front seat.

Next to every cottage but one was a parked car pulled up under the trees. Down in the lake, I could make out the pier and the black swinging wedges of Ollie's leaky rowboats. A few yellow lights gleamed from the dark cottages onto the green, wet leaves of the trees.

"Well, there she is."

Our lights swept over the rear of a starboard-leaning, green-shingled, screen-enclosed cabin. Above the back door, painted on a weathered two-by-four, was the evocative appellation HAVEN OF BLISS. All of Ollie's other cottages had names, too: BIDE-A-WEE, REST-A-SPELL, DEW DROP INN, NEVA-KARE, SUN-N-FUN.

We inched under the trees. My father switched off the Olds. With a great, gasping shudder, she sank into a deep stupor, her yearly trial by fire half over. The rain was coming down hard now, pounding on the roof of the car and dripping off the trees all around us. I tumbled out of the back door—plunging into mud up to my ankles—and began sloshing my way down through the wet bushes and undergrowth to the lake. Behind me, I could hear my kid brother already whining that the mosquitoes were biting him. There at my feet, lapping quietly at the rocks, the black water faintly aglow, was Clear Lake.

In the darkness a few feet offshore, I could dimly make out our wooden boat, the waves slapping against its side.

K-thunk . . . K-thunk . . . K-splat . . . Plop . . . Plop. . . . One of the most exciting sounds known to man.

"Hey, come on! We gotta unload! Everything's getting wet!" my father shouted down through the trees.

I slogged back up the path, splopping and slipping and skidding and cracking my shins against tree stumps. My father and mother were tugging at the tarpaulin that covered the luggage rack on the roof. The rain poured down unrelentingly.

"Where the hell's the flashlight? Don't tell me we forgot the FLASHLIGHT!"

"I thought you brought it," my mother answered from the dark deluge.

"OH, JESUS CHRIST! WHAT THE HELL *DID* WE BRING?"

"Well, you made up the list."

"How the hell can your forget the FLASHLIGHT?"

"Well, if you had gotten up when you said you would, you—"

"SHUT UP! I don't have no time to argue. This stuff's getting soaked!"

My mother disappeared into the cabin. "The lights aren't working," she called out into the rain a moment later.

My father didn't even bother to answer that one. If

she had said the roof was gone and there was a moose in the bedroom, it wouldn't have surprised him. He staggered past me, reeling under an enormous cardboard box full of pots, pans, baking powder, rubber ducks and ping-pong paddles.

"Don't just stand around. *Do* something!" he bellowed to everyone within hearing. "DAMN IT, DO I HAVE TO DO *EVERYTHING?*"

I grabbed a beach ball from the back seat, waded through the clay and groped my way up the rickety back steps. Inside, the cabin smelled of rotting wood, wet shingles, petrified fish scales and dead squirrels. My father had struck a match, which dimly lit up the worn linoleum and bare boards of the kitchen.

"Why the hell didn't Ollie turn on the juice? That's what I want to know!" he raged, flicking his match around in the dimness.

"Hey, here's a kerosene lantern!" my mother said excitedly. Above the tin sink, on a shelf, stood a dusty glass lamp half full of cloudy yellow oil.

"OUCH! DAMN IT!" The match had burned down to the old man's thumb. Sound of fumbling and scratching and cursing in the darkness. Finally, another match flared.

"Gimme that lousy lamp."

He lifted off the black, smoky chimney and applied the match to the wick, turning up the knob on the side as he did so. It sputtered and hissed.

"DON'T BREATHE ON THE MATCH!" he yelled.

At last the wick caught hold and a steady blue-yellow flame lit up the primitive kitchen. We rushed out into the dark and for the next hour lugged wet sacks, bags, blankets, fielders' mitts, all of it, into the kitchen, until at long last the Olds, a ton and a half lighter, shook itself in relief and settled down for a two-week rest.

My mother had been sorting it all out as we dragged it in, carrying blankets and bedding into the little wooden cubicles that flanked the kitchen. When it was all indoors, the old man stripped off his soaked shirt and sprawled out on a lumpy blue kitchen chair.

"Well, here we are." He grinned, water dripping down over his ears. "Boy, am I hungry!"

My mother had already opened a can of Spam. We sat amid the boxes, downing two-inch-thick sandwiches.

"We gotta set the alarm, because we wanna get out real early to fish," announced the old man between bites.

My kid brother was already asleep in the next room.

"If ya wanna get the big ones, ya gotta get up early!" His eyes gleamed brightly in the glow of the kerosene lamp. "They always bite good after a rain. Yessir!"

But it was all back in the garage—my rod, my reel, my father's tackle box, his bobbers, his Secret Gypsy Fish Bait Oil that he had bought from the mail-order catalog.

"But, Dad, don't you remember I told you. . . ." I began miserably.

"So how come I found it on top of the car? I wonder who put all that fishing stuff on top of the car? Hmmmm . . . . I guess somebody must have snuck up and put it on top of the car when you weren't looking."

Ten minutes later, I lay in the dark, ecstatic with

relief and expectation, huddled under damp blankets and a musty comforter. The rain roared steadily on the roof— as it would for the next two weeks—and drummed metronomically onto the bare wooden floor beside my bed.

K-thunk... K-thunk... Plop... Plop... Plop....

The boat called to me from the dark lake. From somewhere out in the woods, something squeaked twice and then was silent. My kid brother tossed and whimpered softly from beneath his pillow; and across the room, my father's low, muttering snores thrummed quietly in the night. We were on vacation.

THE STAR-CROSSED ROMANCE
OF JOSEPHINE COSNOWSKI

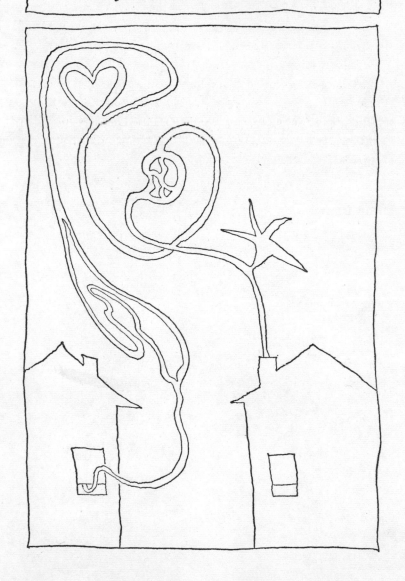

Lustiki! read the marquee in letters three feet high. Must be Lithuanian for lust, I mused, jogging from foot to foot to keep warm in the long line of Manhattan art-film fanciers in front of the East Side's smart new Cinema 69, their ascetic faces flushed in anticipation of another evening of artful montages, elegant pans, gracefully executed dissolves. I glanced at the posters that rimmed the box office. One of them read:

LESBIA, AN IDEALISTIC YOUNG PEASANT GIRL, TRAVELS TO THE BIG CITY IN SEARCH OF TRUTH. STARRING LUD-VICKA BELLICOSNICK AND DIRECTED BY MILOS PEDER-ASTINCKI, THE 13-YEAR-OLD SENSATION.
"A SEARING EXPERIENCE" . . . NY TIMES "SMASHING"
. . . REX REED

Lesbia herself, bosoms ripe as Indiana cantaloupes, her peasant eyes widely spaced in her magnificent Slavic face, appeared to be enjoying a transcendental sexual climax with a Viet Cong irregular.

The throng around me looked like a Fellini crowd scene: squat females in leather jackets carrying bull-whips, coveys of razor-thin, trilling creatures of inde-terminate sex in velvet jerkins and elf shoes, a few scowling, bearded revolutionaries in full Zapata attire, their denim jackets abristle with OFF THE PIGS buttons. The light from the marquee glinted from the polished lenses of hundreds of pairs of rose and blue sunglasses, some as large as dinner plates. A sizable contingent of Shoshone Indians in beaded headbands and fringed deer-skin jackets exchanged mystic signs, their voices oddly Bronx-tinged as only CCNY braves' can be.

Others were clad in castoff costumes from Joan Craw-ford pictures: padded shoulders, frumpy skirts, sequined wedgies, ringlet curls and feather boas. Here and there a Grand Concourse version of Humphrey Bogart sneered condescendingly at the mob, cigarette drooping sardoni-cally from a lower lip. A few Belmondos and several Warhols added vivid accents to the mosaic. A Salvation Army Santa Claus at the curb, his Kriss Kringle costume hopelessly *démodé*, rang his bell listlessly above the clamor. I tugged at the bill of my Jackie Coogan tweed cap, setting it more firmly on my head as I shivered slightly under my Clint Eastwood paisano serape, my Fred Astaire two-tone patent-leather pumps pitifully in-adequate to the December slush.

After the show—which turned out to be a flawed but compelling black-comedic existential skin flick in the drolly amusing Sacher-Masoch genre—I eased into a booth at Le Bagel Vérité, a favorite haunt of cinemagoers in the neighborhood. Sipping a mug of mocha absinthe, described on the menu as the favorite of John Barrymore, I found myself studying a striking poster on the wall amid the likenesses of Paul Newman, Marlon Brando, Peter Fonda, Ché Guevara and Charley Brown. It was my old friend Ludvicka, "Don't I know you from someplace?" I reflected, the absinthe flowing like tepid lava through my veins.

Of course! It hit me. Every male I ever knew believed that foreign girls, even if they're just from the next town, were infinitely sexier than the ordinary homegrown product. I laughed ironically in my Sidney Greenstreet manner, as I often do when my mind takes a philosophical turn. Then, painfully, it all began to come back—my own almost forgotten adventure in alien sensuality, foreign passion, forbidden fruit.

It began innocently enough a couple of weeks before Christmas in the northern-Indiana steel-mill town where I festered as a youth. It was just before Christmas vacation, already deep into a bitterly cold winter, and I was shuffling idly through clots of drifted, soot-covered snow, my mind drifting aimlessly like a semi-deflated blimp. I was between romances. A brief, disastrous fling with Elizabeth Mae Longnecker had petered out in late November, when I discovered she wore earmuffs and galoshes with snaps. Somehow she had seemed *different* on the tennis courts.

I was coming home late from band practice, my

left shoulder still aching from the weight of my sousaphone, lips tingling from the last 24 bars of *The 1812 Overture*, when I sniffed a pungent aroma that was to play a dramatic part in the erotic history of my kidhood. I sniffed again. It was vaguely familar, yet strange—and mysteriously exciting.

· The elusive aroma mingled with the rotten-egg smell of the Grasselli Chemical Works, the swamp-gas exhalation of the Sinclair refining plant, the smoldering, metallic miasma of the blast-furnace dust that formed our daily breathing air.

As I got closer and closer to home, the aroma grew even lustier.

It was then that I noticed *lights* coming from the Bumpus house next door. The infamous house had been empty since the moiling Bumpus clan, a mob that made Genghis Khan's hordes look like a Cub Scout Jamboree, had stealthily departed in the night with their blue tick hounds and their gallon jugs of corn likker, leaving unpaid rent and a yard full of garbage behind. I looked curiously at the lighted windows. After the Bumpus family, there was no telling *what* might show up. I went up our back porch and into the kitchen, already feeling a vague, rising excitement.

"HEY, MA. . . ."

"How many times do I have to tell you to take off your overshoes out on the porch?"

"Yeah. Ma, who . . . ?"

"I said take 'em off on the porch. Now! Look at my floor!"

I went back out on the porch, kicked off my overshoes and darted back into the kitchen. My kid brother sat at the kitchen table, glaring sullenly at an arithmetic book.

"Hey, Ma, who moved in next door?"

She didn't answer, being busy at the moment sliding a meat loaf covered with tomato sauce into the oven. The radio on the refrigerator whined:

> *When the deep purpulll fallz*
> *Over sleepy garden wallllzz. . . .*

"Would you turn that radio down? I can't hear a word you're saying."

Flushed after her usual struggle with the oven door, which had a bad catch and hardly ever closed right unless it was slammed four times, my mother straightened up and wiped her hands on a kitchen towel. I reached up and turned the radio down just as the back door opened and in came my old man, snow showering off him as he stamped and snorted.

"Holy Christ, it's cold enough to freeze off a brass monkey's. . . ."

"Please. The kids are listening." She caught him just in time.

"Hey, what the hell's that I smell? You cookin' somethin' new for supper?" he asked suspiciously, being strictly a meat-and-potatoes man who viewed all divergences from that basic menu as an effete affectation. He truly believed that the only food people really liked was meat and potatoes and that they just pretended to like other things in order to impress each other.

"It's coming from next door," my mother answered absently as she set the table.

"Next door? Y' mean they're actually cookin' supper over at the Kissels?" His voice rose in disbelief. Lud Kissel, our other next-door neighbor, had given up eating food years before, about the time he discovered bourbon, on which he subsisted entirely except for periods when he had to settle for gin. Since he had given up eating— and working—the rest of the family lived on cornflakes.

"No, from the Bumpus house."

"THE BUMPUSES!" He blew up, rushing to the window. "Don't tell me them bastards are back! Goddamnit, if I have to kick another of them lousy hounds. . . ."

One of his worst fears was that the Bumpuses would move back next door, just to drive him crazy. The memory of that shiftless swarm of tobacco-spitting, raw-boned, gimlet-eyed primitives was still an open wound in my father's psyche.

The heady aroma from next door filled our kitchen like a cloud of exotic gas. Suddenly, without warning, as the old man peered into the darkness, a loud musical thumping, heavy and rhythmic, added to the clamor.

"What the hell is that?" The old man's voice was tinged with trepidation. We remembered all too well the sleepless nights we spent while the Bumpuses' ever-twanging Victrola filled the night air with the nasal sounds of Ernest Tubb, the Delmore Twins and Cowboy

Copas. It was the first note of a barrage of thumpings that was to continue for some time.

"Well, here we go again." My father slumped into his chair at the kitchen table and opened a can of Atlas Praeger.

"I think I know what that smell is," said my mother with quiet authority.

"Yeah?"

"That smells to me like stuffed cabbage."

The old man looked up from his beer. "It does smell like stuffed cabbage. But there's somethin' else." He sniffed the air.

"I think they're cooking blood soup, too." My mother said it as if everybody cooked blood soup every night.

"*Blood* soup!" My father gagged briefly on his beer.

"AAAGGHH!" My kid brother had joined the discussion. He was a notoriously picky eater.

"Yes. Irma Kissel says they're Polish."

"Boy, that's a relief!" The old man said it like he meant it. "For a second there, I thought we had the Bumpuses back. Sometimes I get nightmares dreamin' about all that guitar playin' and them dogs yappin', and that old bastard spittin' tobacco juice into our driveway."

POLISH! I thought, suddenly alert. "Do they have any kids?" I asked.

"I'm not sure, but I think there's two or three boys. And. . . ." she stirred the mashed potatoes expertly, salting them lightly with her left hand, ". . . I believe there's a girl."

My father had lost all interest in the subject and was

deep in the sports page. As long as the Bumpuses weren't coming back, he didn't care who moved in.

A *girl!* A *Polish* girl! A wave of ecstasy shuddered through my frame. Our neighborhood was singularly lacking in girls of any kind. For some reason, practically every kid in the neighborhood was a male. The only place we ran into actual girls was at school, and they all lived in mysterious neighborhoods far from ours. Of course, there was Esther Jane Alberry, squat, truculent and morose; and there was Helen Weathers, who had hair like a football helmet and who weighed 200 pounds soaked in sweat, which she almost always was; and there was Eileen Akers, in her thick glasses, who spent all of her time at the library. But they didn't count. Though Schwartz, Junior Kissel and I talked a lot about girls, it was mostly hypothetical.

"Her name's Josephine," said my mother. "She's about your age. She goes to All Saints School."

I struggled to maintain my composure, but inwardly I reeled. My god, the jackpot! A Polish girl my age had moved next door to me!

A prime universal belief among my peers was that the girls of the next town, East Chicago, were fantastic, and that the most fantastic of all were Polish girls. There was never any scientific evidence. It wasn't necessary. It was just an established fact. Sometimes when Flick got his old man's car, we'd go to East Chicago to ride around with the windows open just *looking* at Polish girls walking around the streets. We'd holler out at them and ride around and around the block, jabbing each other in the ribs, swigging Nehi orange, gulping down White Castle hamburgers and blatting the horn. This sport was called skragging for some reason. We never actually talked to a girl, of course, or even really got near one; we just hollered, gunned the motor and stared.

"Josephine?" I tried to sound unconcerned, as though I hadn't caught the name.

My mother ladled out the gravy as she said, "They call her Josie. Their last name's Cosnowski. They come from East Chicago."

God almighty! Wait'll Schwartz and Flick hear about this! Josie Cosnowski from East Chicago! A new era had begun.

At lunchtime the next day, the following dialog took place at a fashionable greasy spoon called John's Place, which catered to the high school crowd and featured the gristliest hamburgers in Christendom:

SCHWARTZ (*mouth full of French fries*): "I bet you couldn't guess what I'm gettin' for Christmas."

FLICK: "This ketchup is rotten. It's all clotted on the bottom." (*Hollering loudly over general hullabaloo and 400 watts of jukebox.* "HEY JOHN, HOW ABOUT SOME FRESH KETCHUP HERE? THIS BOTTLE'S BEEN ON THE TABLE FOR SIX YEARS!"

SCHWARTZ: (*persistently*) "You wouldn't believe what I'm gettin' for Christmas."

FLICK (*standing up at his stool and waving ketchup bottle*): "HEY JOHN, KETCHUP OVER HERE FOR THE TROOPS!"

JOHN (*a short, swarthy man of uncertain parentage and evil temper due to a life of continual harassment by acne-plagued adolescents and a succession of short-order cooks who quit every three days*): "Who the hell's hollerin' for ketchup?"

FLICK: "Me. Over here." (*Ketchup in bottle, still being waved, suddenly unclots, spraying surrounding customers, including renowned defensive halfback who rises menacingly from his stool and then settles back, figuring it isn't worth it.*)

HALFBACK: "Watch it, punk."

JOHN: "I don't have ten arms, kid. Here's your damn mustard."

FLICK: "I wanted ketchup."

JOHN: "Oh, fer Crissake!" (*Disappears into smoky blue kitchen, where loud crash has just occurred.*)

SCHWARTZ: "Yep, this is gonna be some Christmas."

ME: (*hearing Schwartz for the first time through my daydream*) "Hmm?"

SCHWARTZ: "What's the matter with you? You got the crud or something?"

FLICK (*resigned to his fate, scooping mustard out of bottle with finger and smearing it on cheeseburger*): "You got the crud? Stay away from me, man! I don't need no crud."

ME: "Crud? Who's got the crud?"

JOHN (*reappearing from kitchen trailing sweat and lugging tray of hot roast-beef sandwiches*): "Who wanted the ketchup here?"

FLICK: "I had an uncle once almost died of the crud."

JOHN: "WHO WANTED THE KETCHUP?"

HALFBACK (*to Flick*): "Hey, Shrimp, you wanted the ketchup, right?" (*Grabs ketchup from John, pours half a bottle on Flick's cheeseburger.*) "That enough? Or wouldja like a little on top of yer head?"

ME: "Pass the ketchup, please."

HALFBACK: "You trying to get smart, kid?"

SCHWARTZ (*oblivious*): "I think my old man's getting me a power saw."

HALFBACK (*shoving ketchup bottle toward me*): "Just watch it, kid."

FLICK: "He caught it in Indianapolis, at the Y.M.C.A."

ME: "Caught what?"

SCHWARTZ: "Yessir, I'm gonna mount it on my workbench."

JOHN: "Which one a you gets the coffee malt?"

FLICK: "Here."

JOHN: "You two guys get the Cokes, right?"

ME AND SCHWARTZ: "Yeah."
(*BRIEF PERIOD OF GULPING.*)

ME: "You guys know the Bumpus house?"

SCHWARTZ (*chewing on an ice cube*): "Don't tell me?"

ME: "Tell you what?"

SCHWARTZ: "That good old Delbert Bumpus has moved back. One a them stinkin' Bumpus hounds bit me so hard one day on my paper route, I thought I'd die. That mutt hung onto my leg for two blocks."

ME: "No. Somebody else moved in." (*I paused dramatically, with impeccable timing.*) "A girl."

FLICK: "A what?"

SCHWARTZ: "That crummy hound waited for me every day and . . . a girl?"

ME (*nonchalantly sipping my Coke, milking the suspense*): "Yep. A girl." (*I bit off the end of a French fry.*) "She's Polish."

The effect was galvanic. Flick looked up from his malt, something he rarely did, face blank with wonder. Schwartz, his hand palsied, slopped Coke on the counter.

ME: "From *East Chicago*."

SCHWARTZ: "A Polish girl? From East Chicago? Next door to *you?*"

FLICK: "What's her name?"

ME: "Josephine. Josephine Cosnowski."

The three of us sat silently for a long moment, each lost in his private thoughts. Already, schemes and fantasies were rushing through our respective skulls.

174

HALFBACK: "Did you say Cosnowski, kid?" (*Obviously he had overheard our entire conversation.*)

ME: (*warily*): "Yeah."

HALFBACK: "That's what I thought you said." (*He took a huge swig of root beer, burped menacingly, hitched up his pants and swaggered out.*)

SCHWARTZ: "What was that all about?"

ME: "Search me."

FLICK: "You never can figure what them jocks are thinking. If anything."

That night after school, Flick, Schwartz, Kissel and I sauntered casually past the Bumpus house—as casually as we could with the temperature five below and the wind howling through the telephone wires like the sound effects on *I Love a Mystery*. We slogged along in our overshoes, pretending there was nothing at all unusual in the fact that we had paraded up and down in front of the Bumpus house 12 times in the last ten minutes.

"I'll bet she's fat," said Flick his breath swirling in the arctic air.

"You sure are lucky, living right next door. You can probably look right in her *bedroom*," muttered Schwartz bitterly.

I peered up at the house, hoping for a glimpse. I could still see the scuff marks on the front door where Floyd Bumpus had kicked it in the night he and old Emil, his father, had the fistfight that Emil won by hitting him with a tire iron. The place looked the same, but it was different, somehow. Now it was a *girl* house. It kind of radiated femaleness. The steady thump of polka records shook the frozen ground beneath our feet, and the seductive aroma of stuffed cabbage filled our nostrils. It was almost dark and the streetlights were coming on up and down the block when Junior Kissel made the first score.

Flick had just picked up a chunk of rock-ice and was about to throw it at a shivering sparrow huddled on top of a garage. I was busily trying to scratch my left shoulder blade because my sheepskin coat always itched through my shirt. Schwartz was bent over hooking his galoshes.

"There she is!"

We stood poised in the icy air, like some diorama of *Ancient Man at His Daily Tasks* in the Museum of Natural History. The side door of the Bumpus house had opened and two figures emerged into the gloom: a short, lumpy lady with a shawl over her head, and behind her, barely visible in the darkness—a girl! She had on a parka with those rope hooks which were very big that year. The lady picked up something next to the basement stairs, and together the two of them disappeared back into the house.

For a half-minute or so, nobody said a thing. Finally Flick tossed his ice chunk in the general direction of a streetlight and Schwartz whistled a low, quavering note.

"Well, I saw her first," said Kissel.

I didn't say anything. But I knew what I had to do. There was no turning back.

Every night before I did anything else, I had one chore to perform. I was supposed to go to Pulaski's store to buy whatever my mother put down on a list. It wasn't really every night: just whenever she didn't feel like doing the shopping herself in the afternoon; but it was often enough to be irritating. Tonight was a store night. On the way through the darkness, as I cut across a vacant lot, I imagined how I would meet Josie. She'd fall off a ladder and I'd catch her. I'd dribble a basketball in the gym and crash into the stands—right into her lap. Or a bus would run up on the sidewalk with a crazed driver at the wheel, and I'd scoop her up just as the wheels were about to. . . . Men think these things.

I went into Pulaski's store, still in a misty daze. The usual mob of steelworkers crowded the joint. Pulaski sold a lot of chewing tobacco and work gloves. Pulaski himself toiled behind the glass meat counter, his apron stained with grease and blood. Howie, his current clerk, a guy who used to work at the Esso station, glared at me from behind the grocery counter. Grubby kids huddled around the penny-candy case, as I had done in my long-gone youth. I had played softball with Howie before he had become permanently angry working at the gas station and Pulaski's. He didn't go to school anymore, just worked and drove around in Pulaski's panel truck, delivering potatoes and sacks of groceries.

"Whaddaya want? And be quick about it, fer Crissake."

He worked 19 hours a day, and everyone thought he

was lucky because he didn't have to go to school any-more. He had a thin, red, hawklike face. His hair was a kind of mustard yellow, and it stuck up all over his head like worn-out paint brushes. He was famous because he'd had to quit school over a girl. He had just made the basketball team in the middle of his sophomore year and then suddenly he had dropped out and gotten mar-ried. After that, he was always mad.

"Gimme a loaf of Silvercup." Pulaski's was not a self-service store. He kept everything safely out of every-body's reach.

"Large or small?"

"Large."

I read off the rest of the list and Howie packed every-thing into a paper sack as the crowd eddied around me.

"Oh, yeah. And a Mr. Goodbar." At that stage of the game, I was completely hooked on Mr. Goodbars. There was something about the way the chocolate mixed with the peanuts when you crunched your teeth down on it that got me where I lived.

Howie shoved the candy bar toward me. He knew I usually ate it on the way home, and it didn't go into the sack. I handed him the money and he savagely hit the keys on Pulaski's cash register.

"Goin' to the game Thursday?" I asked, passing the time of day.

"Are you kiddin'?" That was his standard answer to almost everything. I guess he felt that the world kidded him a lot.

My frozen feet propelled me unsteadily back toward

178

home. I had made this trip so many times that my body moved totally on its own. The street lamps were festooned with the plastic wreaths and electric candles that the town put up every year. Sometimes they didn't take them down until April. A giant semi boomed past, cascading gray slush up over the sidewalk.

I slogged across the street and began to cut through the vacant lot, thinking of the basketball game on Thursday, only four days away. Basketball is Indiana's true religion. Nobody thinks of anything else from the opening game of the season through the state finals, and then they argue about it all summer long. This was the big game with our hated rivals, the Whiting Oilers, a well-named team. They came from a school buried amid a jumble of refinery tanks and fumes. Understandably, they played a hard, vindictive game. I already had my ticket in my wallet. It was the big game of the year.

I was about halfway across the vacant lot, crunching contentedly and clumping along the well-worn path, when I saw something ahead of me in the darkness. I hardly ever met anybody on the path, so I stopped for a second. It looked like some kind of bear, a low dark blob in the gloom. I'd always felt that one day I'd meet a bear someplace, but I never thought it would be here in this vacant lot. I couldn't make out what the hell it was. It seemed to be sort of lunging around, making sounds. I was about 20 or 30 yards away from it, maybe a little less. Deep in my sheepskin pocket, I felt for my Scout knife and edged forward.

For a couple of seconds I had a powerful urge to turn

and run like hell, and then I saw what it was. It was somebody picking things up off the ground. I walked forward warily, because Grover Dill used this path, too, and he was dangerous in the winter because the cold made his teeth hurt.

It was a girl. It was Josie! It *had* to be. No girl in our neighborhood looked like *that*. She was bent over picking up cans and packages from the path and trying to stuff them into a torn paper bag. She looked up. The light from the neon sign at the Bluebird Tavern illuminated her face in a flickering radiance. I almost fainted. These moments are known to all men: the electric instant of manifest destiny: Ahab sighting Moby Dick, Tristan meeting Isolde, John meeting Yoko! She stuck a can into the tattered bag, and it rolled out into a snowdrift.

"Hi." It was all I could think of to say. She said nothing, just continued to scrabble among the weeds.

"I guess your bag broke," I said observantly. Still nothing. She struggled on in the snow.

"Here. I'll help you." It was the first coherent thought I'd had.

And then she spoke, her rich, sensual, vibrant voice coming from deep within her well-filled corduroy coat, from amid the mufflers and the red stocking cap; a voice which to this day I have never forgotten: "T'anks."

Together we packed the torn bag. Her groceries ran heavily to sausages and what smelled like sauerkraut. I could feel a surge of erotic tension warming my longjohns. Together we marched on through the darkness, occasionally dropping a can or a bottle.

"Uh . . . what's your name?" I didn't want to tip my hand and let her know I had been stalking her relentlessly for days.

"Josephine." She didn't ask mine—a bad sign.

"Where do you live?" She didn't answer, being busy at the moment retrieving a turnip that had rolled among a collection of beer cans.

"You want a piece of candy?" I asked, hoping to soften her up for the kill.

"What kind?"

"Mr. Goodbar. It's got peanuts."

"They stick in my teeth," she said, her breath making a misty, fragrant cloud.

I kept looking at her sideways, and every time the streetlight hit her I couldn't believe that such a girl had moved into our neighborhood. Her high, chiseled cheekbones, the dark hair trickling from under the stocking cap, the rounded slopes and valleys of her corduroy coat, the faint scent of cabbage—all were beginning to tell on my addled senses. But my mind was alert and sharp, guarding against a false move. I could sense that this voluptuous creature must be carefully handled. She could fly into the wilderness forever if I so much as struck a wrong note. With Esther Jane Alberry, it was a hit here, a kick there, a hurled snowball and nothing more. But I sensed something in Josephine that opened up pores in my soul I never knew I had.

"Boy, it sure is cold," I said finally. I figured I was

on safe ground. Somehow I knew I had to keep her talking.

"Yeah. I'm sure glad we don't have to go far," she answered, sniffing in the cold air. I saw my opening.

"Where do you live?" I tried to sound totally uninterested.

"Right down the street. Third house from the corner."

"Oh. . . ." I struck, hurling the harpoon with all my might. "Well, well. That sure is funny. I live in the second house from the corner. How come I never saw you before?" I lied adroitly.

"We just moved in from East Chicago."

"That's a nice town. What school do you go to?"

"All Saints."

"I go to Harding."

She didn't comment. We were nearing her house. I knew I had to make my move or all would be lost. I couldn't ask her to the basketball game, since I only had one ticket and they had been sold out for over 12 years for the Whiting game. How about the Orpheum? No, I was almost totally broke because of Christmas. I had bought a catcher's mitt for my kid brother.

I started to drag my feet and suddenly I became aware that she was giving me a long, intense stare, her magnificent crystal blue eyes catching the gleam of a passing headlight. I felt silly.

"Would you like to go to a party?" she said suddenly.

Good God! No girl ever asked *me* to a party before, except Helen Weathers once, and that didn't count because she was fat.

"A party? A party? Why, why, yes, sure, uh . . . Josie."

"I don't know anybody around here," she said. "I hope you don't get the wrong idea because I asked you."

"Heh-heh-heh. Why, of course not!"

I couldn't believe it. Polish girls really *were* everything I'd heard! Here I didn't even know her five minutes and she was asking me to a party. At last life had begun. This was it!

We trudged up the front steps of the Bumpus house to the sagging porch where the Bumpus hounds had howled and raged on many an afternoon of summers past and old Emil had fallen through the railing one night when he had a snootful. But I wasn't thinking about that now. She opened the front door and a great wave of warm air redolent with strange aromas—along with the rumble of recorded polkas—came flooding out onto the wintry porch.

"Don't forget the party," she said, holding the door partly closed with her free hand.

"Oh, I won't! I go to a lot of parties. When is it?"

"Thursday. Pick me up about eight."

"Why, I just happen to have Thursday open. Yessir, and. . . ."

She was gone. The door closed. It wasn't until I got back home with the groceries that I realized that she had said Thursday. THURSDAY! There were at least 12,000 people who would have given anything to have a ticket for the Whiting game, but suddenly basketball and the Oilers didn't seem as important as they had before. Sex will do that to you.

The next day I told Schwartz what had happened. "Y'mean *she* asked *you* to a *party? You?*" He practically reeled.

"Yup."

"Boy, them Polish parties are really wild. Casimir told me about one once that went on for four days."

All day in school I drifted on a plane of ecstasy, floating high above the humdrum dronings of history teachers. All through geometry I wrote Josie, Josie, Josie in parabolic curves on the back of my notebook.

That night I began to plan my wardrobe. I laid the stuff out on my bed, checking it carefully. Let's see, I'll use the Old Man's Aqua Velva, and. . . .

The next essential was getting my father to let me use the car. A car was absolutely necessary for the operation that was beginning to evolve in my mind. In Indiana, male kids usually start driving at about ten, so I was an accomplished gravel-thrower and was well known at all the local drive-ins hamburger joints from Big Blimpie to the Route 41 Diner.

"Uh . . . Dad. Is there any chance of getting the Olds Thursday?" He was deep in the sports page, which I figured was as good a time as any to hit him for the car.

"Thursday?" He squinted at me, blowing smoke through his nose and letting it curl up in front of his eyes like a shifting curtain. If I hadn't known that he hated movies, I'd have sworn that he studied under Humphrey

Bogart. For all I know, Humphrey Bogart studied under him. The old man got around.

"Thursday . . . let's see. Thursday. What am I doin' Thursday?" He talked aloud to himself, toying with me. I knew Wednesday was his league bowling night and on Fridays he went to the wrestling matches with Gertz and Zudock. Saturday was usually up for grabs, with my mother usually winning when they drove over to visit her friend Bernice and her dumb husband, Elmer, who worked for the phone company.

"What do you have in mind for Thursday?" he asked, folding the paper over so that he could read the scores of the various bowling leagues. His life revolved around three things—the Chicago White Sox, bowling and the Oldsmobile, the order depending on the season.

"Well? What d'ya want the car for?"

Naturally I couldn't tell him what I *really* wanted it for. "Me and Schwartz are going to the Whiting game at the civic center, and Schwartz's old man's Ford is up on blocks."

"Whiting'll kill ya. That Zodnycki's got a jump shot from the keyhole that you can't block, and he hits from the outside, too. They'll murder you guys."

"Yeah?" was all I could say, knowing that the old man was probably right and also that I wouldn't be anywhere near the game, if things went right.

"OK. But be sure to fill the tank. Not like the last time, so you run out of gas in Blue Island and me and Heinie hafta chase all over the place before we find ya. If that wasn't stupid, tryin' to make it to Chicago and back on a gallon of Shell regular. Leave it to you and Schwartz."

He had opened an old wound: the memory of that miserable night when Schwartz had supplied a gallon of gas and I had supplied the car on a disastrous double date that ended with the four of us sitting in the car on a railroad siding at 15 below zero for two and a half hours. The two girls hadn't spoken to us then or since, and I didn't blame them.

"Don't worry. I'll fill it up. I learned my lesson."

"Yeah, I'll bet," was all he said as he went back to the scores.

Well, that took care of that. It was humiliating, but I had the car; that was the big thing. I went to my room and sat down at the desk that I used for my homework. My Aunt Glenn gave it to me for my eighth birthday. It was robin's-egg bue and had yellow bunnies painted on the side. I figured one day I'd paint it red or green, since the bunnies were beginning to be embarrassing. My aunt had a thing about bunnies. For every Christmas as long as I could remember, she'd given me bunny slippers and no doubt I'd get another pair this year, even though my shoe was a half-size bigger than my old man's.

I made out a list of what I had to do:

1. Get haircut.
2. Polish car.
3. Buy gas.
4. Gargle.
5. Squeeze blackheads.

The next day, which was Wednesday, was dark and windy with a lot of snow drifting down all afternoon. We had an auditorium session in which Jack Morton and Glen Atkinson and some other guy dressed up like Wise Men while our crummy glee club sang *We Three Kings of Orient Are*.

"Boy, you sure are gonna miss one hell of a ball game," said Flick as we hitchhiked home from school that night. "That better be some babe."

I said nothing, since it was obvious that Flick was jealous that I had a date with the greatest-looking girl for miles around. For a couple of days now there had been churning inside of me a molten excitement that was getting so hot I could hardly stand it. Every time I thought of her, it started again. I can't explain why, since I hardly knew her, but maybe that's the reason. You never feel that way over somebody you really know.

"Didja hear Zodnycki said the Wildcats are a bunch of overrated punks, and that he and four girls could beat 'em goin' away? I read it in the *Times*," Schwartz chipped in, blowing his breath in a big cloud as the cars rumbled past us. We were part of a tiny contingent of diehards who always hitchhiked the three miles back and forth to school, not only to save our bus money but also out of principle.

"That bum'll be lucky if he cans five points against Sobec," I answered, trying to sound like I cared about the game.

"Ah, I dunno. That bastard must be eight feet tall. And he looks like he's about 40 years old," Flick yelled

187

over the roar of a passing diesel. He spoke the truth. Northern Indiana high school teams often resemble the best the Big Ten can field; 300-pound tackles, blue-jowled and squinty-eyed, are common. Their actual ages are as hard to tell as the sex of a clam. There are rumors that many promising players are not even enrolled in first grade till their 17th year, and by the time they're high school sophomores are grizzled veterans with large families and pro contracts from four leagues.

"Watch this baby." Schwartz waggled his thumb seductively as a knock-kneed Buick rattled toward us. It slowed to a stop. "GOT 'IM!" Schwartz hollered.

We piled into the amiable wreck, which was driven by a mammoth steelworker who was fragrant with beer and chewing tobacco. He spit a long amber skein out the window into the frigid air.

"If yer gonna get in, get in. I ain't got all day!"

The uproar inside the Buick was deafening. No muffler, bad shocks and a transmission that sounded as if it were made of a million cracked iron marbles. The floor of the car was ankle-deep in beer cans, cigar butts and rags—a real working car.

"Hey, Schwartz!" Flick yelled over the din.

"Yeah?"

"D' ya think Ace here is gonna score tonight?"

"I hear them Polish girls invented sex!" shouted Flick.

"You guys are just jealous!" I yelled as I struggled to keep from falling off the seat.

At that moment, I became aware that the driver was

peering intently into his cracked rearview mirror right at me. At the time, it had no meaning.

Just as we climbed out at the end of the roaring ride, the steel puddler spit another stream of tobacco juice and hollered over the clatter of his valves:

"You guys go to high school?"

"Yeah," Schwartz answered for all of us.

"You don't know when you're well off."

He spat again and drove off. It was a point we weren't prepared to accept. It was just before the dawn of the age of youth culture, and being a kid was just something you went through before joining the real world.

"Y' comin' over to the Red Rooster tomorrow night after your date?" Flick asked me. The Red Rooster was where everyone who was with it went after a big night.

"Are you kiddin', Flick?" said Schwartz, jabbing him in the ribs with a mitten. "He's gonna have a lot more to do besides sit around and eat cheeseburgers, right?"

"Now look, you guys, I don't know what you're thinkin' I'm gonna do, but. . . ." I tried to inject a note of dignity into the discussion.

"Don't worry. We know what you're gonna *try* to do. Oh boy! If I had a date with that doll, lemme tell you. . . ." Flick winked a large, lascivious wink.

"Don't worry. I can handle whatever comes up." More elbows in the ribs. I played the game.

I plodded home. There was time before supper to back the car out of the garage in the frigid air and to give her a coat of Duco Seven if I worked fast. I had polished that car so many times that I could do it in my sleep. I was already deep in the middle of a torrid embrace in my mind when I became aware, as my right arm buffed the hood, that a hulking shadow had darkened the gloom around me. It blotted out the distant glow of the open-hearth furnaces against the lowering clouds. As I glanced up, a rasping voice set my teeth on edge.

"Hey!"

A thrill of fear zipped through me. "Uh . . . yeah?" I managed to squeak, dropping my polishing rag into the slush.

"You the kid takin' Josie t' tha pardy t'morra?"

"Yeah."

"I t'ought so." He was wearing a checkered wool jacket about the size of a circus tent. He had on red earmuffs and no hat. He had a crewcut that looked like steel wool.

"Who're you?" I asked. It was a dangerous question, but I couldn't think of anything else to say.

"Whatsit to ya?" He leaned with one hand the size of a 12-pound ham on the fender of the Olds. I didn't like the way the conversation was going, and I wondered if I should make a break for the back door.

"I'm 'er brudder. I jus' t'ought I oughta see who was goin' out wit' Josie."

"Oh. Yeah. I heard of you. She's a nice girl. She sure is a nice girl. Yeah."

Words kept squirting out of me. He reminded me of

Alice the Goon from the Popeye comic strip. I could smell the faint aroma of a locker room.

"You play football," I said, trying to make contact.

"Dat's right, she's a nice girl." He ignored my latest remark as being too obvious to answer.

"Yep. She sure is. A real nice girl. Yep."

"You show her a nice time, y' hear? An' if anybuddy gives ya any trouble, tell 'em ya know Stosh." He made a sound that I guess was a laugh. It sounded like two angle irons clanking together.

"I sure will . . . Stosh."

He clanked again and shambled off into the darkness. I noticed that he had left a dent the size of an elephant's footprint in the fender of the Olds. I should have taken the hint.

Later that night at Pulaski's, I waited my turn amid a crowd of ladies who milled around the meat counter, watching Pulaski as he weighed pork chops. He was famous for his two-pound thumb.

"I said I didn't want 'em so fatty!" bellowed a hulking lady in a stocking cap.

"Whaddaya want from me, lady? I don't grow the pigs!"

An angry murmur arose among the throng as Pulaski held them at bay with his cleaver. Howie struggled past me, carrying a sack of potatoes on his shoulder.

"I hear you're goin' to the party," he said out of the side of his mouth as he hurried past.

"How'd you know?" I threw after him.

"I hear," he answered.

Finally, as I picked up my sack of groceries, Howie leaned over the counter and said: "You're takin' Josie, eh? Well, good luck." He said it in a kind of voice that could mean anything.

"Thanks," I answered in the same voice. He looked tired, as though he had worked 18 hours that day, which he had.

Sure enough, I met Josie on the way home again. This time she hung on my arm and brushed up against me as we struggled home with the grocery sacks.

"I hear you met Stosh." She spoke in a husky, throaty voice, not at all like her brother's.

"He came over when I was polishing the car."

"You'll like him."

"Yeah, sure."

"You'll like my uncles, too. They want to meet you." She snuggled closer as we sloshed through the slush. Somewhere a radio was playing *White Chrismas,* with old Bing Crosby crooning away. We never really had a white Christmas in northern Indiana, since the snow came down already gray from the steel mills, but it was a nice thought. Once in a while we had a fall of rust-colored snow, and that could be kind of pretty once you got used to it.

"Especially you'll like my uncle Stanley."

"Yeah, that'll be great." Inside my gut, those roaring waves of excitement crashed so loud that I didn't realize how sinister it was that all her uncles wanted to meet me. The streetlights played over her magnificent cheek-bones, her fantastic eyes, her coal-black hair. I felt hints of her body, round and soft, through her corduroy parka and my sheepskin coat. I clutched desperately to my bag of groceries.

The great Atlantic salmon struggling thousands of miles upstream, leaping waterfalls, battling bears to mate is nothing compared to your average high school sophomore. The salmon dies in the attempt, and so, often, does the sophomore, in more ways than one. As we ambled on through the gloom, I didn't have the slightest hint of what was coming; neither, I suppose, does the salmon, just does what he has to do. So did I.

"Hey," I said just before we got to her house. "Where is this party going to be?"

She looked into my eyes with that gland-tingling look that can drive a man out of his skull—if he's lucky.

"It's a surprise. You'll have fun."

Instantly I pictured a mysterious, blue-lit den somewhere with writhing bodies and the distant thudding of orgiastic drums. Her smoldering gaze promised everything. I felt deep-down stirrings, and I was glad it was dark. A few snowflakes drifted down between us. She closed her eyes in the dim light. I leaned forward. Our lips touched. My ears roared. Passion rushed in a mighty torrent through my veins. . . .

RRRRRRRIIIIPPPP! I felt my bag of groceries give way. I grabbed frantically at a box of eggs as it hurtled to the frozen pavement, followed by a bottle of ketchup and a jar of strawberry jam. Crash followed crash.

Lightly she breathed, "I'll see you tomorrow . . . darling." And was gone.

Blindly I struggled amid the gray heaps of snow. I salvaged only a half-pound of sliced bacon, one No. 2 can of carrots and a loaf of rye bread. All the rest was ruined or lost. But it was only the beginning.

I was up at seven the next morning, nervous and excited. As I left for school after the usual oatmeal, I tried to catch a glimpse of Josie, but her house was dark and silent. All day at school the talk was about Zodnycki and what he had said about our ball club. Naturally, passions ran high. The Whiting Oilers had always been menacing, but with Zodnycki at the pivot and popping off like that, it was going to be a grudge match. I played it as cool as I could, pretending to be deeply involved in the game. It was a peculiar feeling, since I was normally a red-hot basketball nut and for the first time in my life something else was sneaking in by the side door.

"Hey, you want to sell your ticket?" Schwartz asked after school. "You got a date tonight, so what are you goin' to do with the ticket?"

"I may sell, if the price is right," I lied, since I knew that I never could sell a ticket to one of the big games of the year, even if I couldn't use it. Just *having* the ticket meant something.

"I know a guy who'll give you four dollars, in my biology class."

"Nah, I'll hang on." Tickets cost students a dollar and a half, so four dollars wasn't much of a deal, and I wasn't going to sell anyway.

"Well, you lucky fink, just don't catch anything I

wouldn't catch, ha-ha," Flick yelled out at me at the top of his lungs as I left the crowd on my way home.

"Where you takin' her?" asked Schwartz as the December wind sighed through the telephone lines and the branches of the trees creaked under the load of ice they carried. Just before Christmas, it gets dark early in the afternoon on the Indiana plains. School had just let out and already it was almost dark. Two kids struggled by, pulling a Christmas tree on a sled.

"How 'bout the Dreamland Roller Rink?" Schwartz sarcastically suggested. "Girls love roller skating."

I said nothing, just chucked a piece of ice in his direction and headed home.

"How come you're not eating the creamed onions?" my mother asked at the supper table.

"Uh . . . I'll have some later," I answered. I didn't want any onions lousing up the plans I had in mind. I wasn't hungry. I was out for big game tonight, and food meant nothing.

I went into the bathroom and carefully shaved, and as usual the mysterious Nicked Chin Law went into operation—a peculiar phenomenon that I was not yet familiar with but which later became part of my life. All men know of this and have pondered it. On the evening of every important date, the razor invariably bites deep, leaving rich geysers of spurting blood in its wake. I stuck bits of toilet paper all over my face, attempting to stanch the flow. They didn't help, so I splashed Aqua Velva on my raw jaws. My face sizzled like a halibut on the broiler.

"Yer sure shavin' close for a basketball game," the old man tossed at me as he peered in the bathroom to see how much longer I'd be. He liked to finish the paper in there every night after supper.

"I'll be right out," I said noncommittally.

"Well, just don't take all night," he said, rattling the editorial page.

After the shave I doused myself with Bloode Of The Sheik, a spectacular cologne that my father had won on a punchboard and that came in a bottle shaped like an Arab riding on a glass horse. The label, in jade and gold, read:

"LOVE ELIXIR OF THE EAST . . . 47% PERCENT ALCOHOL."

I sloshed it over my head and down my chest, and instantly an explosive aroma filled the bathroom and clouded the mirror. For a few seconds my head reeled out of control as the love elixir did its seductive work. I staggered out into the fresh air. The mixture of the cologne with Aqua Velva was irresistible.

Meticulously I got dressed, making sure that my T-shirt and Jockey shorts were snowy, my mauve-colored Tony Martin roll-collar sport shirt tucked carefully into my best slacks. Everything had to be absolutely right. This was a historic night. Never again would I suffer the guilt of knowing that I had never really done much with a girl except smooch with her in the balcony of the Orpheum.

I examined myself in the mirror in my room. A magnificent specimen of sophomoric manhood. Bits of toilet paper still clung to my chin. The rich exhalations of the mysterious East rose about me in a purple haze. I was loaded for bear.

Slipping into my mackinaw, I clamped my green earmuffs on my head, wound my precious eight-foot purple-and-white scarf around my neck 36 times—purple and white being our school colors, a combination so adroitly selected as to make all acne-ridden complexions look leprous by day and absolutely necrotic in gymnasium lighting. Casually, yet with a touch of stealth, since the old man had been known to change his mind without warning, I picked up the car keys from the dining room table.

"Don't forget to fill the tank," he bellowed from the next room. I went out into the icy darkness and over to the garage. Tonight I had a date with an actual girl from East Chicago. An East Chicago *Polish* girl. At last, after a measly lifetime of basketball games and double features and French fries at the Red Rooster and Monopoly games with Schwartz and Flick, I was in the big time! I put the key into the ignition and the Olds started instantly, as if it, too, sensed impending ecstasy.

Since Josie lived next door, it wasn't much of a drive over to her house, but I hummed happily all the way as waves of excitement coursed up and down to every nerve ending. The Olds had a gasoline heater that, when it was in the mood, was hotter than the hinges of Hell. I flipped it on. Immediately a great flood of scorching air engulfed my feet and steamed the windows. Hot dog! Everything is going great! I pounded my mittens on the steering wheel in a frenzy as I eased out of the driveway and up to the curb in front of Josie's house. Life stretched before me, a vast unexplored continent of voluptuous abandon. With throttle wide open and a full head of steam, I hurled myself full tilt toward the unknown, little suspecting what lay ahead.

For a full half-minute I sat in the darkness, peering up at the porch through the frosted window of the Olds, composing my mind for the opening ploy. The heater roared. The car felt richly warm and dark. Straightening my earmuffs, I swung out into the cold, leaving the engine running.

I knocked on the front door and waited. Inside, all was silence. I peered in through the heavy curtains that hung at the front windows. Pitch darkness in the parlor, where once the Bumpuses had spent their squalid hours amid pig and chicken, dog and mule, guitars twanging at all hours, hawking and snorting and squatting amid old Montgomery Ward catalogs.

I knocked again, louder. Something seemed to be moving inside. The door opened a tiny crack.

"Who you vant?" A beady eye peered out at me.

"Uh . . . I come for Josie."

Silence. The eyeball glinted piercingly in the streetlight.

Finally: "Josie?"

"Yeah. Me and Josie are going to a party."

"You vait." The eye disappeared.

I stood alone on the windswept porch. For a brief moment, I had the wild urge to flee into the night. In fact, I was just about to turn and make a break for it when the door opened to a larger crack and the same voice, possibly female, said, "You come in. She not ready."

I found myself in the black parlor and was aware of dim, blocky shapes of furniture set with geometric precision about the room. A crucifix gleamed dully from atop an upright piano flanked by what looked like stone urns. I was led through the house and into the darkened kitchen. The overpowering aroma of Polish cooking engulfed me like an octopus. Coming from a family where Franco-American spaghetti was considered an exotic dish, this was enough to make me stagger slightly as I felt my way past the redolent stove.

The figure ahead moved steadily to the cellar door and we descended the steps. Fear clutched at my vitals. At that time I was deep in the works of Sax Rohmer, the illustrious author of *The Claw of Fu Manchu, The Insidious Doctor Fu Manchu,* beside which Ian Fleming and his insipid Dr. No pale to the pasteboard figures that they are. Well I knew that Dr. Petrie had been many times lured into sinister traps down just such a passageway as I was traversing now. We reached the first landing. If I was going to escape at all, it was now or never. But like C. Nayland Smith himself, I allowed myself to be lured into the spider web of foreign intrigue.

For a moment, I was blinded by the bright light of the cellar.

"You sit. You eat."

For the first time I saw that my guide was a short stocky woman wearing a black shawl over her head, her cheeks bright red with peasant health, her eyes a brilliant china blue.

"Me Josie's mother."

A heavy-set man sat at the table, huge shoulders bulging under his uncomfortable-looking shirt. He wore suspenders, something I thought only firemen did. He had a handlebar mustache of such magnificence and daring that he would have been an instant hit in any of today's hippie communes. His thin blond hair was parted in the middle.

"You take Josie to party," he said, his voice heavy and blocklike, like chucks of iron ore clanking out on the table. I recognized instantly that I was in the presence of a first-class open-hearth worker. [Polish steelmen are legendary, and in fact the Paul Bunyan of the Gary mills was a Pole. This could have been Joe Magerac himself, a man capable of personally rolling out hot ingots between the palms of his hands.]

I squatted at the table, surrounded by dishes loaded with boiled potatoes and slices of dark home-made Polish bread. Josie's mother, beaming, shoved a huge white plate of thick foreign china in front of me.

"You like cabbage, yes?"

Josie's father, as I suspected he was, dug into his own plate, a fine spray of juice rising about him as he tucked into his nightly meal. I looked down at my plate, and there before me was a mountainous, steaming portion of God knows what.

"But I already had supper," I protested weakly.

"You eat," she repeated, still beaming happily.

There was no way out. But if this was what I had to do for a night of passion, it was worth it. Taking a deep breath, I took a bite. For a moment, the heady mixture of cabbage, spice and meat was a great, wet wad in my mouth, and then its haunting, incandescent succulence, inevitability and *rightness* hit me where I lived. My God, I had never eaten anything in my life that came anywhere near this; even the chili mac at the Red Rooster, which had seemed to me to be the ultimate in cuisine, wasn't in the same league with this incredible concoction. Across the table from me, Josie's father attacked his second platterful, washing it down with a stein of dark beer. As I wolfed the cabbage down, it was like some long-contained dammed-up secret part of me had broken into the open and was on the hunt.

As I ate I glanced around, noticed chair, tables, couches, chests—a whole *house* in the basement. It was the first time in my life that I had met anyone who lived in the basement and kept the upstairs of their house, I later learned, for state occasions such as weddings, funerals and visits from the taxman. They had painted the furnace, which loomed at the far end of the basement like some multi-armed fairy-tale monster, a bright robin's-egg blue. All the furniture—the wooden tables and chairs and benches—was the same Easter-egg color.

"Josie almost ready," her mother said, pressing a half-dozen Polish pickles on me. Gripped by an uncontrollable rapacious hunger, I ate and ate, spurred on by the slurpings and fork scraping of Josie's father.

"You have good time. You good boy. You like cabbage?" she asked, forking a potato scented with bay leaves onto my plate.

"Cabbage good. I like." I found myself picking up the cadence of their speech.

A huge belch welled its way up from the dark hidden caves of my body. I couldn't control it. It rumbled deep in my throat like a passing freight train laden with smoked hams and late fall turnips. My fellow eater burped amiably through his handlebar mustache and gulped down another two liters of beer.

"You good eater," he rumbled, and I hate to use that word because people are always "rumbling" things in bad books, but he *really* rumbled, the way only a Polish open-hearth worker can.

"Pickle, potato good, too," I mumbled between bites, elbow-deep in cabbage juice and beating down an insane desire to lick the plate.

The next moment my eyeballs were straining at their moorings like two barrage balloons. Josie was with us. She had come down the stairs while I was in mid-burp and sucking a fugitive bit of cabbage from under a back tooth. She wore a dirndl skirt, which at that time was a big deal among high school girls, but she wore a dirndl the way a tiger wears its skin. Her narrow waist flared suddenly into broad, sculptured peasant hips. Above a wide dirndl belt, her embroidery-laced puffed-sleeved blouse—stuffed fuller than the cabbage—billowed and rippled like the heavy white clouds that scud over Warsaw in the spring. I have heard stories of German soldiers after World War Two refusing to leave Poland, being literally dragged home by their heels, protesting every inch of the way. I can understand them. It isn't often that a kid in the sophomore class has a date with an earth mother.

It's hard to explain the combination of the basement, the blouse, the stuffed cabbage, the handlebar mustache and the mysterious shrouded parlor furniture, but all of it made me feel that I was in some kind of exotic delirium. Was the cabbage drugged? Were these actually highly trained dacoits in the pay of a power-mad Oriental? Their eyes *did* look strange, not like Esther Jane Alberry's wholesome Sunday School orbs.

"Hi," was all she said, her voice rich and low like the waters of the Danau flowing past the ancient bridges of medieval Europe.

"Hi," I answered, my rapier wit honed to its finest cutting edge.

"I see my mother's been feeding you," she said, smiling in a way that made my socks itch deep inside my Thom McAn saddle shoes.

"Yeah. It sure was good. Boy. Yessir."

"Josie good cook," said her mother, clearing away the dishes and preparing to serve what appeared to be a plate of spectacular plum dumplings topped with sour cream. "She make cabbage."

"*Josie* cooked the cabbage?" I said stupidly, struggling

to get to my feet and finding, unaccountably, that I seemed to be carrying several cast-iron bowling balls under my waistband.

"She make good wife one day." A claw gripped at my intestines. There was something in Mrs. Cosnowski's eye that I had never seen in the eye of a mother before. I would learn to know that look well in later years. At the time, I thought it was just the cabbage clouding my eyesight.

"Well, what do you say? Shall we go?" Josie asked lightly, touching my arm suggestively with the tips of her fingers.

"You come next, we play pinochle?" Her father stood up, towering above me like a stone god from Easter Island, his head bowed under the ceiling. Seated, he was a human being; standing he became a monument of 6'5" or 6'6", wearing what must have been a size-75 shirt with probably a 22-inch neck.

"I play pinochle good," I answered, which was the truth. We shook hands, or rather I stuck my tiny fist into the vise for a moment or two. My knuckles clattered and snapped.

"Next time Josie fix whole meal. You like." Her mother seemed to think only of food. Josie put her coat on and we climbed the basement steps, groped our way through the darkened parlor and were out on the porch, Mrs. Cosnowski clucking behind us in her native tongue.

At last we were in the Olds, warm and redolent with muffler fumes. I felt her hand resting on my arm as I shoved it into first gear. I had no idea where we were going.

"They liked you," Josie said, her hand squeezing my arm affectionately as she snuggled closer.

"Yeah, they were sure great." I wanted to ask her about the basement scene, but I figured what the hell, live and let live.

"Did you really cook that cabbage?" I asked, struggling with the defroster. She said nothing, but her grip on my arm tightened perceptively.

"Gee, I'm glad you got the car," she sighed. What was she trying to tell me? I detected a double meaning in every syllable, every intake of breath.

"Yeah, my old man lets me have it any time I want." This, of course, was a bald-faced lie. If I had gotten the car every time I wanted it, the old man would have had to walk to work, which was five miles away.

"Well, heh-heh-heh. Where to? Let's get over to that party."

"Turn right on California and I'll let you know when to turn next."

"Who's throwing this party?"

"Ooh, look at the Santa Claus." She ignored the question, peering through the clouded window at a hulking electrical Santa in a store window who seemed to be alternately hitting croquet balls and picking his nose.

We drove on. My anticipation over the approaching party was almost uncontainable. I'd always heard about great parties that other guys went to. They always described them in the clinical detail of a sex manual.

I had even pretended to have been to a few myself, which of course, like most of my life, was a sham and a fraud. The parties I had been to consisted mostly of shoving, standing around and drinking Cokes, turning up or turning down the record player and constantly going out for more potato chips. This pulsating creature next to me, so full of life and stuffed cabbage, obviously offered far more than potato chips.

The Olds banged along as it always did, bottoming familiarly in and out of potholes.

"Turn right!" she said suddenly. Her hand clutched sensually at my arm as I wheeled the Olds into a lumbering right turn, clunking over the rutted ice. I couldn't figure out where she was taking me. I didn't know anybody from school who lived in this neighborhood. We rolled past the Ever Rest Funeral Parlor And Furniture Store, its green-and-red neon sign glowing bleakly onto the snow.

"Tell me when," I said, trying to sound like Robert Cummings.

"Turn left here." Like most girls, she gave directions in retrospect, invariably telling you to turn just after you've almost passed the street. I spun the wheel wildly. A scurrying panel truck bounced in and out of the ruts, trying to avoid me. I caught a brief glimpse of a swarthy face mouthing obscenities. We crawled up a darkened street.

"OK. You can park here."

Cars were parked on both sides of the street and in a parking lot on my left. I eased into a slot. For a brief moment, I squeezed her hand in the dark, and her lips brushed my ear. Then we were out in the cold and going up some kind of gravel walk between snow-covered shrubbery. I could see in the darkness a great stone-turreted building. I thought, God almighty, I've hit the jackpot! I could see the headline: "ORGY AT WEALTHY HOME. TEENAGERS ARRESTED." I saw other people going in a side entrance, and brief flashes of light from within. We stood now in the gloom cast by a vast stone façade. Gargoyles leered from black nooks wearing tiny caps of crusted ice. Josie's eyes gleamed with an exalted light. NO! I thought, it CAN'T be!

It was. The heavy wooden door swung open and we stepped into the vestibule of St. Ignatius R. C. Church. A throng of pious merrymakers eddied somberly around me. I had been euchred beyond human depravity. I had been tricked into a church Christmas party, something I had avoided like the plague for all of my atheistic years.

"Ah, my son, we haven't met you, have we?" A bald priest wearing gold-rimmed glasses leaped forward, taking my hand and clinging to it for a long, agonizing moment.

"Ah, I see you're with our little Josephine. Ah, yes, I remember her baptism, and now she's a grown lady and bringing her young man here for us to meet. Well, we'll grow to know each other well, my son, and. . . ."

Her young man! We'll grow to know each other well! What is this? Our little Josephine stood at my side, her arm linked in mine, eyes shining.

"Yes, Father, he could hardly wait to get here."

I looked her full in the face, expecting to see a wink, some sign that she was kidding, but no! A look of benign piety glowed on her magnificent face. I began to feel like the worm in the apple, a butterfly on the pin. The crowd moved forward, the priest greeting newcomers and pointing me out. I heard snatches of conversation: "Josie's young man," "My, one minute they're babies and the next you're marrying them. . . ."

Heavy men with mustaches and ladies with shawls beamed at me. Hundreds of little kids bumped and milled at my knees. From somewhere in the bowels of the church, I heard a deep steady thumping. We moved on in the great throng, downstairs, through corridors, the thumping growing louder and louder. Again I was seized by a paroxysm of fear, some instinct telling me to flee before it was too late.

And then it *was* too late. We were in a huge room heavy with the scent of sweating bodies and Polish cooking. The heavy rhythmic thumping made the floors jar, the walls shudder. Sweat coursed down my shoulder blades. Josie grasped my right hand.

"Darling, do you dance?"

I was known as a particularly tenacious dancer in my somewhat limited set, but I had never seen anything like this. On a stand on one side of the room, dressed in suspenders, funny pants, embroidered shirts and plumed derbies, were Frankie Yankovic and His Polka All Stars, thumping out the *Dawn Patrol Polka,* a particularly insistent and violent example of the genre.

I was yanked almost off my feet by a single powerful motion of Josie's left arm. Her beautiful feet thumped the floor maniacally. I bobbed up and down like a yo-yo on a tight string. Elbows jabbed me in the ribs, deep and hard. I caught brief images of sweating faces, clumping feet. Frankie Yankovic and His All Stars—led by Frankie himself, playing a mother-of-pearl accordion—rose to thunderous heights that would have made coleslaw out of the most powerful electronic rock groups. Every third beat, feet rose and fell like great balls of concrete.

For some unaccountable reason, I discovered I was a consummate polka dancer. The polka is a true soul dance. You don't learn it; it engulfs you and sweeps you on in a flood of braying cornets and tootling clarinets and the thundering syncopation of bass drums and cymbals. The drummer, a heavy-set Pole, squatted like a toad and his equipment, operating with the machinelike precision of a pile driver. I bounced and sweated, Josie clinging and hopping, ducking and bobbing as one born to the beat. As we danced she seemed to grow progressively more alien and foreign.

In the midst of the 23rd chorus of the *Stars and Stripes Polka,* as we swirled past a group of shawled ladies standing like vultures along the wall, I caught a glimpse of a pale, harassed, hawklike face. We swirled around the floor again like a merry-go-round out of control. Deedledeedle *BOOM* Boom deedle deedle *BOOM* Boom! The drummer's heavy foot rose and fell like an air hammer, booming out the bass notes.

Again I saw that white, pinched face staring directly at me like some despairing ghost. It was Howie. *Howie!* Our eyes met. He was trying to tell me something. I saw a round little fat girl clinging to his elbow and around them, like so many toadstools around a rock, three other short, squat children, noses running, some crying, some yelling, all with the look of Howie around the eyes. Old Howie, who could handle a basketball like Bob Cousy. Howie, who had worked 18 hours a day at Pulaski's, lugging potatoes and weighing salami, ever since he married his Polish girlfriend.

It was then that I knew I had to get out of there fast. Josie was wearing some kind of perfume that must have been brewed by the Devil himself. The more she danced, the headier it became; but I was impervious to its siren lure, for every time we spun around, I saw Howie standing there like a dead man stood among the shawled women with his round little wife and his brood.

Frankie Yankovic did a rippling riff on his squeeze-box to signal a brief break in the gymnastics. Even though I was in top shape and had been playing basket-ball, football and Indian wrestling for months on end, I was wheezing badly.

"I'm so glad we came. You're going to like the Father. He's a wonderful man." I saw large numbers of the cele-brants pushing their way into the next room, where there seemed to be some sort of table set up.

"Uh . . . I'll get us a drink or something, OK?"

Josie was now in confidential conversation with a girlfriend. They appeared to be talking about me. Her girl-friend nodded in what looked suspiciously like approval.

"I'll get a couple of Cokes. And one for your friend."

Josie smiled. Like a greased pig. I darted off through the doorway, threading my way through the crowd like a halfback on an off-tackle slant. I edged past a table where nuns were selling gingerbread men and cider. Again I caught a glimpse of Howie, who looked more harassed than ever as he handed doughnuts around to his crowd of kids. It was a sight that chilled the marrow. I worked my way up a stairway against a stream of people who were working their way down. I was in the vestibule, moving like a shadow. And now I was at the door.

Suddenly, without warning, a heavy weight descended on my left shoulder from behind. For an instant I thought I was having a paralytic stroke brought on by too much dancing. Some immense force spun me counter-clockwise. A great hulking form blocked out the rest of the room from my vision.

"Uh . . . hi, Stosh."

He looked at me with a kind of joyous hunger flicker-ing in his beady eyes, the way a Kansas City lineman must look when he's closing in on Joe Namath.

"Yuh havin' a good time wit' Josie?" he asked rhetori-cally.

"Yeah! Sure! Great!"

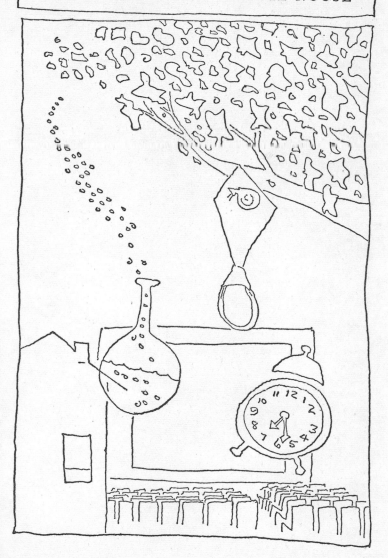

Why does a man become a revolutionary? Just when is that precise instant of stark realization when he perceives with unmistakable clarity that he is but a humble tenpin in the cosmic bowling game of life? And that others are balls in that game? Look closely into the early private life of any great revolutionary and you will find a girl. Somewhere along the line, a pair of elfin eyes put Karl Marx down so decisively that he went home and wrote the first words of his *Manifesto*. I well remember my own turning point. Like most pivotal moments in our lives, it came unexpectedly and in the guise of rare good fortune. Her name was Daphne Bigelow. Even now, ten light-years removed from the event, I cannot suppress a fugitive shiver of tremulous passion and dark yearning. Her skin was of the clearest, rarest form of pure, translucent alabaster. She had no "eyes" in the mundane sense, but rather, she saw the world, or the world saw her, through twin jade-green jungle pools, mirrors of a

215

soul that was so mysterious, so enigmatic as to baffle ninth graders for yards around. I hesitate to use such a pitifully inadequate word as "hair" to describe the nimbus of magic, that shifting cloud of iridescence that framed a face of such surpassing beauty that even Buddha would have thought long and hard before staring straight into it. Why I go on with this self-flagellation I do not know. Nevertheless, I cannot but continue.

There was something else about her, something I am not quite sure I can adequately convey through the sadly lacking means of imperfect human language. Daphne walked in a kind of soft haze of approaching dawn. A suggestion always lingered about her that she wasn't there at all. Rosy gold and blue tints flushed and were gone; soft winds blew. Somewhere exotic birds called out in their sleep as Daphne drifted into Biology I, trailing mimosa blossoms and offering ecstasies not yet plumbed by human experience.

Way down deep among the lower one third of the class, amid that great rabble of faceless mankind who squat among the rancid lunch bags and musky galoshes of academe, who are forever condemned to view the great pageants of life from parked third-hand jalopies amid the apple cores and beer cans of drive-in movies, I sat hardly daring to hope—from over a gulf so vast as to make all earthly distances pale to triviality—and devoured her daily with my eyes from behind a Biology I workbook.

Throughout the entire first semester after she came to Hohman High, my wonder grew like some dank, unclassified toadstool in the coalbin of my subconscious. At first, dimly and with naïve joy. I believed myself to be secretly blessed. I watched for her face everywhere: in the halls, on the stairways, in auditorium crowds, in the sullen herd who waited numbly outside the doors to be admitted in the early-morning hours, in the rumbling hordes who poured out of school after the last classes. Everywhere. From time to time, she would drift briefly into view and then disappear. Her name never appeared on those lists of kids involved in what are known as "activities." She was above that. As day after day faded forever into history, as my intricately contrived glandular system ripened and matured, so my carefully concealed passion for Daphne Bigelow burgeoned, until finally it engulfed me and I was swallowed up like Jonah into the inky blackness of the whale's belly.

The midsemester exams came and went. Over Christmas vacation I had been haunted by nameless fears, since Daphne was out of my sight. Now a new terror—would I be assigned to the same biology class with her next semester? Finally, the dread day arrived. I could scarce credit my senses. Not only had Daphne biology teacher—a dapper gentleman wearing rimless Bigelow condescended to remain among us; our new glasses, black shellacked hair and squeaky shoes, named Mr. Settlemeyer—had, in an exquisite moment of insight and compassion, assigned Daphne Bigelow to me as my Biology II lab partner! Together we would investigate the mysteries of the great animal kingdom of which we were but a small part.

Well do I remember that blissful afternoon when, together, Daphne and I pinned a limp, formaldehyde-dripping frog to a cork specimen board and I, being the man of the house, bravely took up scalpel and showed her the stuff of which I was made. At the head of the class, Mr. Settlemeyer, pointer in hand, described various portions of frog anatomy, while beside me Daphne smiled with the faintest suggestion of approval, of perhaps even admiration, as I rose to magnificent heights of skill and daring. She averted her eyes delicately as I performed the autopsy. Her tiny *moues* of girlish fright and squeamishness drove me on to even greater pinnacles as I laid bare the vitals of the unfortunate amphibian. We both received an A+ for the afternoon's work.

From that deceptively unprepossessing yet starkly symbolic beginning, our love took root and grew. By the end of the third week we were on a first-name basis. This may seem a small achievement, but it is not every man who is privileged to call a genuine goddess by her first name, and to be answered in kind.

I learned more about her every day, but mostly from outside sources. She spoke little of her home life, her joys, her aspirations, her dreams. While I, being a male, babbled on endlessly, weaving about both of us a rich cocoon of myth and gradiose philosophical generalities.

As winter silently faded into the soft sensuality of early spring, my resolve strengthened and took specific form, though I never saw Daphne outside of biology class. Officially, that is. Unofficially, I shadowed her like a maniacally devoted dacoit, one of the sinister footpad tribe of early India. Watching her from afar, I cataloged her every movement. I covertly made a note of every article of clothing she wore; her wardrobe was immense and infinitely varied. My maroon corduroy slacks, meanwhile, a holdover from the Christmas before, grew increasingly repugnant to me. My purple pullover sweater, with its faded, block-lettered "H," somehow did not sing to me as it used to.

Daphne never rode the school bus or the streetcar, or hitchhiked home like me and Schwartz and Flick. She just magically disappeared. One day I thought I saw a fleeting form enter a long, black, waiting Cadillac down the block from the school, but I could not be sure it was she.

When we passed in the halls, I always wore my carefully rehearsed, debonair Fred Astaire smile, evincing private amusement at this unexpected coincidence. But she always smiled back even more enigmatically as she drifted past—always alone and aloof from the grubby, normal kid hoopla of high school life.

The time for the spring dance was fast approaching. It was the custom for dates to exchange invitations well before the event. Posters appeared. Mickey Iseley a big-name local band, was engaged to officiate. I decided to lay the groundwork for a move so daring, so hazardous that if I had ever confided my scheme to Schwartz or Flick, they would have immediately wrestled me to the ground, hollering that I had finally completely gone off my nut. But I had not breathed to a soul, even to myself, that I had designs on the most magnificent woman in all of Hohman High, if not of the known universe. Few common gophers ever entertained designs on prize-winning, thoroughbred fillies. I did, and learned a lesson that I have never forgotten.

One night, while safely huddled in the familiar lumpiness of the bed I had slept in ever since I had first crawled out of the playpen, staring up into the blackness—the faint sounds of distant, romantic whistles on trains bearing magic people off into the mysterious outside world drifting in through the cracked window shades and limp curtains of my bedroom—I decided to bestow my invitation to the big spring dance on Daphne Bigelow. My mind reeled with the mere thought of it! Craftily I began to piece my plan together. First I must have a date—a casual, everyday date—with her, and from there, inevitably, I would lead her to that dazzling ballroom where our love would finally be consummated in the throes of a dance I had zealously perfected in long hours of loose-limbed, sweaty practice, a dance that I knew neither Daphne nor any other woman alive could ever resist: the lindy. Among my peers, those who really appreciated subtle creativity, the beauty of the withheld statement, my lindy knew no rivals.

The next day my sardonic, martini-dry wit during Biology II flickered like a flame as Daphne hunched next to me over a huge night crawler that together we were dissecting, the heady aroma of her exotic French perfume blending provocatively with the rich fumes of preserving alcohol and dead worm. My courage grew as my bons mots became more and more epigrammatic. Oscar

Wilde would have stood tongue-tied in my presence. And then, casually, amid a brilliant analysis of Mr. Settlemeyer's teaching deficiencies, I prepared to drop my bomb.

"Oh, say, Daphne—heh, heh—pass me another roundhead pin."

Snakily I watched her from the corner of my eye as she turned her gaze away from the benighted night crawler and reached her delicate hand, with infinite grace, over to the pin box. For a moment, panic almost stilled me. Her beauty was such that it took the breath away. Rallying quickly, however, I plunged on:

"Ah—heh, heh—"

I took the pin from her hand, the light brush of her fingers over mine sending goose-pimples all the way down to my Argyle socks and out the ventilation ports of my Keds. Without thinking, I did it. It came out in a rush.

"Howaboutyouanmehavinadate?!"

Instantly, I bent over my friend, the deceased denizen of the underground, a distinct ringing in my ears as the classroom faded from my consciousness and I stood alone, unafraid, in the bull ring. From somewhere off in the hazy distance I heard a flutelike voice say softly:

"What?"

Did I detect a note of incredulity, or was it my imagination? I repeated my question, not daring to so much as glance at her. After a three-century pause came the answer.

"When?"

From a distant auditorium, the school band struck up

The 1812 Overture. Cannons roared; bugles blew. I had scored beyond my wildest dreams! The rest of the conversation went by and is now mercifully lost from memory. But I remember mumbling something about a John Wayne movie, and that I would pick her up. She told me where she lived. The next night, a blessed Friday, was going to be *it!*

Realizing that there was much to be done and no time to lose, like an arrow loosed from the bow, I shot homeward the instant the doors of our pen were grudgingly thrown open. Closeting myself immediately in the bedroom, the scene of so many sweaty erotic daydreams, I went over every item in my vast wardrobe, carefully calculating piece by piece how best to achieve the magnetic effect I knew was necessary. Overlooking nothing, including my American Legion Ball left fielder's uniform, I considered, weighed, rejected, wavered; selected each tiny link in my crucial costuming for what was to prove a fateful night. Individual socks were pored over with infinite care, held up to the light, smoothed and laid reverently aside for a final screening.

Through my locked door filtered the usual family sounds: pots banging, my kid brother's occasional whimper, and finally, the roar of the old man's Olds up the drive. The shadows darkened and lengthened. At last my ensemble was complete. If the outward man has any shield against the slings of outrageous fortune, I was more than ready.

Now I was at the supper table, ready to let the family in on what could very well be a turning point in all our lives. My old man, seated to my left in, as usual, his long underwear, dug lustily into his meat loaf—which, as usual, he chopped up into small pieces, the better to mix with his mashed potatoes and peas, over which he splashed a heavy puddle of lush, piquant Heinz tomato ketchup.

My kid brother, his snout buried deep in his plastic Mickey Mouse Drinkee Mug, slurped noisily at his Cocomalt, which he attacked with a venomous hatred, recognizing the stuff for what it was—a cheap trick to get him to drink milk. The nightly fight that preceded this ritual had come and gone before my arrival at the table. As he drank, he performed the daily rite that my mother referred to as "playing with your food." For some obscure reason, he had found that mashed potatoes, meat loaf and red cabbage tasted better when molded into the shape of an inflated football. He occasionally varied this pattern by constructing other symbolic structures such as propellers, and once even a fairly good likeness of Tillie the Toiler. He then asked everybody:

"What does this look like?"

Nobody ever told him. Our family did not use that kind of language at the table.

My mother shuttled between the stove, the sink and her chair, wiping up debris from around my brother, refilling my old man's coffee cup and in general keeping the action going. In the midst of all this, I asked casually, of no one in particular:

"Do you remember one time I told you about Daphne Bigelow? In Biology II?"

My mother, not accustomed to actual conversation from

anybody, at first did not grasp the meaning of what I had said, thinking that I had asked for more gravy. The old man, who rarely listened to anything said in the kitchen, banged his cup down with a clank on the white-enamel table as a signal for more coffee, a beverage to which he was passionately dedicated. I began again:

"She sure is a great girl."

Behind me, the refrigerator chugged and squeaked to itself, a sound that provided night and day a musical obbligato to our lives. My kid brother had extended his tongue to its fullest length, at least a foot and a half. He was using it to make great sworls in his red cabbage.

"Stop playing with your food!"

My mother slapped him smartly on the arm with a wet dishcloth and shoved a fork into his greasy mitt. Silently he glowered straight down into his plate to announce that it was going to be another of those nights. There were times when he was fed through the use of a funnel and a ramrod, my father prying his teeth apart with a screwdriver while my mother poured the turnips into him. Absent-mindedly, my father, glancing up from the sports page, said:

"Girl?"

"Daphne Bigelow."

My mother, now seated and trying to wrench the Mickey Mouse cup from my brother, who had placed it atop his head, asked:

"Who?"

"Daphne Bigelow."

"STOP FOOLING AROUND AND EAT!"

My father raised his head again and asked:
"What about her?"

Bracing myself for the big plunge, I looked meaningfully around the table at our tiny brood wallowing happily at the trough.

"Well, me and Daphne Bigelow are going on a date. I'm going to take her to the Orpheum to see John Wayne in *Hearts Aflame at the Old Corral*. She's really a great girl."

It was out! Irretrievably!

"I'm going to take the bus and go over—"

The old man cut in:

"The *bus?* Where does she live?"

No kid in the neighborhood had ever dated anyone who lived more than 150 feet away from his own warren. The idea of taking a bus to a girl's house was a truly revolutionary concept, and I knew it. Picking my words carefully, I laid the javelin home.

"Oh, she lives over on Waverly Street. On the North Side." The North Side! In one breath I had evoked an image of a land, a world so remote from ours, so inaccessible as to be almost outside the realm of reality. I might as well have said the North Pole. The North Side was a legendary fairyland of vast lawns, great elm trees and sprawling fiefdoms reached only by winding private drives through landscaped wonderlands.

My father, recognizing instantly the emergence of a new and possibly dangerous generation being nurtured in the bosom of his own home, was now alert and intensely interested. My mother lay back, suspecting a trick.

He asked:

"Did you say Daphne *Bigelow?*"

"Yeah."

"On *Waverly* Street?"

I had struck pay dirt. I played him like a rainbow trout on opening day.

"Yeah. She's in my Biology II class."

My mother, not fully realizing the import of what she had heard, fuzzily threw in:

"What happened to Esther Jane?"

The faintest trace of an enigmatic smile curled the corners of my lips. My father carefully smoothed out his *Chicago Herald-American.* He folded and refolded it with exaggerated care, and then said:

"Daphne Bigelow. I wonder if she's the daughter of Mr. Bigelow over at the Second Calumet Region National Bank?"

"Isn't he that tall, thin man at the second cage?" asked my mother. My father, radiating disbelief from every pore and speaking with some wonder, said:

"No. He's the chairman of the board."

This was news to me! But at the time I did not fully grasp what *kind* of news it was. I was to find out all too soon.

At the time, I thought a chairman was somebody who sat at a desk holding a gavel. I had no idea what a board was, other than the two-by-fours that Flick and I stole from time to time to use in various ways.

"Maxwell Bigelow is the guy who gave that ice-skating

rink to the park," said my old man. He was looking at me now with a very funny expression on his face.

"Oh, it can't be the same one. Does anybody want any more mashed potatoes before I put them back on the stove?" When confronted with inexplicable developments, my mother often pretended that they didn't exist.

"You've got a date with his daughter?" My father slowly stirred his coffee, steaming and black.

"Yep. We're going to a show."

"How did you get a date with her?" my mother asked.

"She's in my biology class. I asked her."

With infinite care and deliberation, the old man placed his cup on the tabletop. He was not a veteran Edgar Kennedy fan for nothing.

"You mean to sit there and tell me"—he paused dramatically—"that you just *asked* her?"

"Yep."

"Maxwell Bigelow's daughter? Maxwell Bigelow from the Second Calumet Region National Bank's daughter? You just *asked* her for a date?"

"Yep."

"Well, I'll be damned!"

Upward mobility had at last hit Hohman. It was the first recorded instance in Indiana of its occurring at the grassroots level.

My mother, who had been gradually sucked into what she now saw was a situation that even more mashed potatoes would not change, decided to go along with it.

"Well, you be *nice* to her parents."

I never quite understood what she meant by this ad-

227

vice—which she always handed out over the years. On various occasions she had advised me to "be *nice*" to teachers, to people on my paper route, to steel-mill foremen, and later even to first sergeants; all people or institutions that she recognized to be in absolute authority.

She continued: "I don't want anyone to think you weren't well brought up."

"Well, I'll be goddamned!" The old man, who had played such a large role in Bringing Me Up Well used this favorite expression to cover all occasions.

"Yep, I'm taking her to the Orpheum. And the Red Rooster afterward."

"Well, don't you keep her out too late so that her mother and father will worry." With that, my mother concluded her entire catalog of counsel about life and its problems. She took it as it came, and felt that as long as you were nice along the way, things would work out fairly well, provided you got home early enough.

All through dessert—her famous rhubarb rice pudding —technical matters of transportation, dress and behavior were discussed. Obviously I had scored heavily, and the awe that they felt about this unparalled achievement slowly gave way to righteous pride.

My old man unbuttoned the top of his long underwear and began to talk of great dates *he* had had in his feckless youth. In sullen silence, my mother cleared the dishes off the table and resumed her old station, hanging over the sink, Brillo pad in hand, amid the lingering aroma of red cabbage, meat loaf and coffee grounds. The squeaking of the refrigerator blended with the sound of Bing

Crosby singing about some Hawaiian babe from the radio in the next room. I began to feel my new status.

By bedtime, as I checked over my outfit for the great adventure. I found myself—for the first time in my life—a full-fledged hero in my own home, not an experience one has often, I have later found. But being a kid, of course, I was under the impression that this was only the natural state of affairs.

Later, in the dark, incredibly witty things to say to Daphne tumbled end over end through my churning mind. I sifted through my assortment of jazzy stories, which I had picked up from the ball field and the gym. In the dark I could see my lean-flanked figure escorting Daphne to a seat in the fabled lushness of the Orpheum. And then—whisked magically—we were in the number-one booth next to the jukebox at the Red Rooster. Casually I drop a coin in the slot, and amid admiring bursts of applause, I demonstrate my matchless lindy, waving casually for Bucky the counterman to knock together another of my specials. Daphne, her eyes shining in unabashed adoration, poured out her heart to me. Squeezing her hand, looking deep into those jade-green jungle pools, I knew at last the meaning of true soul communication. The night was full of laughter, song, dance and awakening love, all against the backdrop of soft spring skies—and, of course, the clean thrust of my chiseled jaw.

Waves of ecstasy coursed up and down my body as I tossed on my monastic pallet. Outside in the darkness, a few distant rumbles of early spring thunder mingled with the soughing of the eternal train whistles reaching into the dark, going away, coming closer, going away again. A few drops of rain pattered on the rusty screen outside my bedroom window. Gradually I fell asleep, but not without a struggle.

At first, as I awoke in the gray-green light that trickled in through the battered window shade and the roar of sparrows holding their morning orgy filled the room with whooping and hollering, I did not remember what day this was. Then I noticed my Number-One, Heavy-Artillery, Important-Occasion Sports Coat hanging on the back of my bedroom door, and I knew. This was D day.

I dressed absent-mindedly in my school clothes, my mind deep in scheming. At the breakfast table the aura of wonder was still rich and ripe. As I spooned in the oatmeal, my kid brother abortively tempted to wrest from me the glory that was rightfully mine by relating some trivial cock-and-bull story about a silly pumpkin he had drawn at school and that was being hung on the bulletin board. I smiled tolerantly and headed off for school.

That morning, when I joined my hitchhiking companions, my fellow freeloaders who every day pocketed—and squandered—the dime that was given to them by their parents to ride the school bus, it was all I could do not to tell them that although I was briefly among them, I was no longer *of* them. Flick particularly, that morning, seemed to be not only disrespectful but somewhat insolent. He had gained some degree of fame on the hitchhiking corner by an alleged exploit which, at least according to his overblown account, he had shared with a certain Juanita Clobberman. I, naturally, did not pull him up short, knowing full well that when the word got out that I had had a date with Daphne Bigelow—in full public view—there would be no question as to who was who and what was what among the hitchhikers.

I approached biology class, however, with certain trepidations. Perhaps she would chicken out. But no, it was like any other day, a routine class. As I crouched over our pickled grasshopper, Daphne was as cool and detached, as chillingly beautiful as ever, but now, deep inside myself, there was a mounting conspiratorial excitement that could not be denied. Almost at the very end of that session, in my most urbanely offhand manner. I came straight to the point:

"Uh—heh, heh—what time shall I pick you up? Ah . . ."

She smiled that faint extra-dry lemon twist of a smile, which to this day I remember above all smiles that have ever been aimed in my direction.

"Tonight?" she asked. An ice pick of fear jabbed up my spinal cord. She paused and went on:

"Oh, any time."

"Ah—how 'bout after supper?"

"Supper?"

Without knowing why, I knew that already I had ticked off a foul ball.

"Oh, you mean *dinner,*" said Daphne.

Dinner? Dinner was something we had in the middle of the afternoon, on Sundays, Thanksgiving, New Year's

Day and Christmas. It was always eaten with the sun high, around three P.M., after which, immediately, my old man, his belt opened, lurching across the living room, burping loudly and bellowing, "Boy, am I stuffed!," would topple over on the sofa and instantly plunge into a snoring coma. I did not, therefore, see how I could pick Daphne up after dinner, and decided to play it safe.

"Well, uh—how about seven-thirty? We can catch the eight-twenty show."

"That'd be nice."

She smiled, and we returned to the world of the grasshopper, the cricket and the cockroach. The rest of the day passed in a kind of dreamy delirium. Bells rang, chalk scratched, basketballs swished through hoops, papers were passed from hand to hand, poems were read, questions asked. School droned on.

At last I was home. Into my bedroom I went. Every item of clothing I had selected the night before I carefully rechecked twice, going back over my entire wardrobe to be sure that in my enthusiasm I had not committed a sartorial *faux pas*. I hadn't.

"NOW DON'T ANYBODY TOUCH ANY OF THIS STUFF!" I shouted out into the hall.

My mother's pans rattled; my brother stolidly threw a ball against the side of the house out in the driveway as I went into the bathroom to begin the meticulous ritual of ablution that would result in a vision of masculine beauty so blinding that there could be no conceivable chance for anything but a spectacularly triumphant evening.

Carefully examining my face, the door locked tightly behind me, I worked with a surgeon's dispassionate skill over my usual blossoming array of bruises, blackheads and what my father called "old juicers." Applying steaming hot water between operations, I worked steadily, until finally there shone out of the bathroom mirror the fresh, pink, beaming image of dynamic handsomeness.

I leaped into the shower. This was an important enough occasion to warrant a second shower for the week. The water roared, and I spread a thick, vibrantly aromatic layer of pungent Lifebuoy lather over my Olympian torso. I had read enough ads to know what happened to those who Offend. I took no chances. The water ran alternately hot and cold, until finally I stood as pure and clean as the driven snow in the heady steaminess of the bathroom, buffing myself down briskly with a terrycloth towel. Reaching up to the top shelf of the medicine cabinet. I took down my father's can of Old Spice talcum powder, a gift that he had received many Christmases before and never, to the best of anyone's knowledge, used. I shook billowing clouds of its cloying sweetness down over me; dusting, brushing here and there, smoothing, anointing myself.

Stealthily using his heavily guarded razor, I then shaved myself to the veritable quick. All 17 of my downy golden fibers, undiscernible to the naked eye, washed down the drain with the shaving lather and warm water. My leonine mane of manly auburn hair, which had been thoroughly shampooed, I now massaged with a heavy elixir of what my father scornfully called "bear grease," a concoction put out by Vaseline to abet the ambitions of countless generations of Midwestern Lotharios. Its scent was more of a direct statement than a suggestion, being violent, highly volatile and—some said—inflammable when in close quarters.

Now came the most crucial task of all. I was known far and wide for my "cute wave," which did not come easily. Dragging a comb through my greasy locks, I began to mold my classic Grecian coiffure. Time and again I redid my masterpiece, only to be driven, as the true artist always is by the elusive dream of perfection, to start anew.

At long last, there I stood: the finished product, American manhood at its ultimate. Teeth agleam, seven pounds of carefully sculptured hair, exuding all the aromatic mystery of a thousand mingled scents enveloped in a palpable nimbus of pure Lifebuoy, the soap of those who care for others. As a final fillip, I gargled at great length, swirling it about my mouth voluptuously—a generous draught of Listerine. Well I knew of The Pitfalls of Halitosis, a dread disease that had struck down many a burgeoning romantic career at its very inception.

Springing light as a gazelle into the bedroom, I began to don my armor. Layer upon layer, I carefully girded my loins. Zero Hour was rapidly approaching. Tonight I would skip supper. First, a crisp new pair of Jockey shorts that I had kept concealed in my drawer for just such a state occasion. I debated briefly about whether or not to wear a T-shirt, finally deciding that I was sexier without. My white-on-white dress shirt, which I had received as a birthday present and worn only for genuinely high moments in life, was painstakingly unbuttoned. I admired its vast, razorsharp, seven-inch-long collar points, its Tony Martin high-rise, its crackling, crisp French cuffs. Pulling it on inch by inch so as not to create the slightest wrinkle, I buttoned it, using only the tips of my sanitary fingers. Then, reaching into my dresser drawer, I brought out the most effective weapon of my arsenal, a pair of magnificent bull's-eye cuff links, each link a great bull's eyeball outlined in dazzling gold. I loved to hold them in certain lights; they seemed to glow—a malevolent, baleful, virile shaft of masculine aggression. True, they made movement of the arm rather difficult, since their combined weight was several pounds, but it was worth it.

Now the tie. A thing of transcendent beauty. It had been given to me as a graduation present from eighth grade by my Aunt Clara. Tying my widest, fattest, sharpest Windsor knot—about the size of a man's fist—I drew it up under my collar with geometric precision. A glittering opalescent silver-gray, 100-percent satin, five and a half inches wide at its fulcrum, it bore in its center the hand-painted image of a beautiful red snail, and hung tastefully well below my belt. It was the greatest tie I had ever seen.

My slacks were a rich chocolate brown, high and pinch-waisted, beginning just under my armpits. They cascaded down over my loins, my kneecaps, and finally clung tenaciously to my ankles. Billowing, pleated, alligator belted, they were the slacks of a man who worked in the lindy as other artists worked in marble. I thought briefly of wearing my golden key chain with the emerald initials, but decided tonight I would underplay. Voluptuously, I then drew on my gray-and-maroon Argyle socks, and then neatly tied a perfect bow on each lace of my perforated, Scotch-grained-leather, full-dress, blunt-toed, crepe-soled bluchers; burnished to a high gloss, the rich dark-red Thom McAn cordovan leather glowed in the gloom of my bedroom.

There are moments of dramatic climax in the rite of dressing. Mine came when I donned my greatest pride—my sports coat. With infinite care, so as not to wrinkle my cuffs, I drew each waffle-weave woolen sleeve down clutched by the fingers, tugged at its low, sweeping hem, squared its massive, looming, horse-hair-packed shoulders, straightened its fashionable six-inch delta-wing lapels, and finally fastened its tasteful mother-of-pearl button. It lit up the entire room, its unique electric-blue shade sending off a lambent radiance of such promise, such rare, delicate aesthetic excitement as to crown my entire ensemble.

Rummaging through my socks in the little drawer of my dresser where I kept my secret papers, I hauled out my invitation to the spring ball. Carefully I tucked it into the inner pocket of my coat. After all, this was the reason for it all. Tonight I would present Daphne with the ultimate gift!

Walking carefully so as not to disturb a hair of my billowing pompadour, I ambled into the kitchen—not without some difficulty, since I had to inch sideways through my bedroom door to squeeze my enormous padded shoulders into the next room. The applause was deafening.

"Wow!"

My kid brother, openly awed at my entrance, raised his head dripping from the mound of creamed chipped beef into which he had burrowed—chipped beef being the regular Friday-night chef-d'oeuvre of our weekly menu. My familiarity with this epicurean dish was to prove invaluable basic training for my later years in the Army.

As I walked in—a veritable human Christmas tree—the pulse of family life noticeably quickened.

"My, you certainly look nice." My mother approved.

"Do you think you'll see Mr. Bigelow tonight?" my father asked, always hoping for an opening, some slight crack in the wall between us and real life outside.

"I don't know," I answered, breathing Pepsodent, Listerine and Sen Sen into the already rich mixture left permanently in the air of the kitchen by millions of boiled cabbages, fried bacon, souring milk and moldering dishrags.

"See if he looks like he does in the pictures in the paper," the old man said.

"Well, I better get going."

I glanced up at the clock hanging over the stove, a clock of purest white plastic made in the form of a large chicken, with two red hands. It didn't have actual numbers to mark the hours; instead, golden plastic letters marched around the rim spelling out: "It hasn't scratched yet." My mother had gotten the clock by saving Bon Ami cleanser labels. It was considered the most beautiful thing in that part of the house.

237

"Well, I'll see you."

My father smiled proudly; my mother smiled proudly; my kid brother stared blankly, chewing slightly. With a casual flick of my left hand in farewell, I slipped out into the night. It was a cool evening, with just the slight edge of winter coldness to it, the kind of night made for warm bodies snuggling together, for dark exchanges of deep thoughts, out of the wind, away from the unfriendly night.

Under the streetlight two blocks away, I waited for the cross-town bus, little realizing that a man named Charon would be at the controls. As I waited, not daring to move lest I disturb a crease, a button, a single undulating wave, I watched the mundane neighborhood life go on around me. The Bluebird Tavern halfway up the block flung open its doors briefly. A flash of light and Mr. Kissel reeled out into the darkness, his unmistakable starboard list instantly recognizable even at 200 yards. And there was Pulaski's Bull Durham sign on the wall of the old candy store (where I had spent many an hour of my callow youth in mortal combat with Old Man Pulaski over the purchase of jawbreakers, JuJu Babies and root beer barrels), looming high against the glow of the steel mills on the horizon. I could barely make out the familiar slogan under the massive bulk of that subtly humorous old bull on the sign: HER HERO. I looked up at him; he looked down at me. We were both in the same business.

The bus slammed to a stop, breathing out hot air and carbon monoxide. In I went, dropping my fare into

238

the box with the practiced nonchalance of the true sophisticate, a man of the world out on the big town. There were no other passengers in the bus that night: I had my choice of seats. I sat immobile, protecting my razor crease, for the entire journey—through darkened streets, traffic, long stretches of used-car lots, junk yards, machine shops, car barns, gas stations, gray battered houses huddled in the shadow of monstrous gasworks. On and on.

Gradually the neighborhoods changed, until at last I was on the North Side. The bus rarely stopped now. Few got on or off except an occasional maid or elderly people carrying little bundles. Somehow the night was different over here: darker and yet more exciting. I watched the trees grow thicker and higher outside the bus window— hedges and graveled walks, until finally we reached my stop. I got off, and the bus roared on. Again I was alone under a streetlight. There were no Bull Durham signs. Mr. Kissel was light-years away. Even the street sign was different from those on the other side of town; a kind of carved Olde English sort of plaque swung in the breeze under the short, stubby little street lamp: WAVERLY STREET.

Daphne had told me that her house was the third one from the corner, on the right. I followed the broad, grass-lined sidewalk into the night. The air fragrant with well-tended lawns, rare budding tulips, freshly graveled drives. Here the houses were not hard by the street but, rather, buried deep in the velvety blackness; a glow-ing yellow light through the trees, here a glint of silver there a splash of blue. I drifted on, knowing that at last I had reached a safe harbor, the world I had always known was mine.

There is something about the smell of well-being that is a balm for the most savage of souls, and yet contains the vaguest whiff of nameless dread. Now I stood at the foot of a curving asphalt ribbon that wound through a grove of overhanging trees, weaving between sculptured beds of rich loam. A small white sign read simply, BIGELOW. No street number, no explanation; just BIGELOW. The lure of the unknown, Circe calling from the rock, enticing ancient sailors to their doom—it was all there, beckoning; but in the American night, what 15-year-old with seven dollars in his pocket knows of this? Or cares?

It was one of those porches modeled loosely after the Lincoln Memorial: Neo-Greek and noble. I felt the tiniest twinge of fear, like the faint beginnings of a toothache. Never, outside of a Viven Leigh movie, had I seen anything like this. A bronze lantern hung amid the snowy vastness, casting a soft amber glow on the welcome mat before a stained-glass door—carved, sparkling, gleaming. The rest of the veranda trailed off into the blackness to the left and right.

I knocked. Nothing happened. I knocked again, peering through the colored panes into a hall; dimly lit, arched and vaulted, silent. I knocked again. It seemed as though I had been under that amber lantern for perhaps a month, maybe more, before I noticed a tiny carved-ivory button sunken into one of the fluted Doric columns that framed the vast doorway. A doorbell. I pressed. After a discreet interval, floating as if from a vast distance away, came the sound of two chimes. Then silence. I waited. The sound of approaching footsteps. Finally the door swung open and an elderly man dressed in black stood in the gloom.

"Master Shepherd?"

"Yeah . . . I . . ."

"Miss Daphne is expecting you."

I followed him down a short, wide flight of stairs to a vaulted hallway lit by a giant crystal chandelier and then through two sliding oak doors into an enormous, darkened chamber lit here and there by glowing bronze lamps.

"Won't you sit down? Miss Daphne will be down presently. I'll tell her you're here."

"Uh—thanks."

He disappeared. I sat on the edge of a high-backed leather chair that looked as though it had been hand-carved by a Spanish conquistador. I looked around. Books with leather binding, thick and wide, ran from floor to ceiling, fading off into the distance. A mammoth carved desk of black wood lit by a small green lamp stretched along one wall. Above it, a tall man with white hair, wearing a black suit, holding a book in one hand, his other resting on a dark-brown globe, looked down at me with a faint, familiar smile from a gigantic painting. I looked again. It was Daphne's lemon-twist smile.

A distant voice filtered down the curved, arching staircase that disappeared upward in the hall. Somewhere a light went on. I caught a glimpse of a long table, sparkling crystal, snowy-white linen, the kind of table and glassware I had seen only in the movies.

Then, suddenly, through the door came a tall, gray, dignified man. For a minute I thought he was the one in the portrait, but no, not quite. I rose. For the first time, I noticed that my shoes squeaked. His face was jovial, pink, a few white hairs over the ear, his suit brown, striped, elegant.

"Hi there. You're here for Daphne, aren't you?" he asked, sticking his hand out toward me, thumb skyward. It was the first time a grownup had ever offered to shake hands with me.

I yanked my mitt out of my right pocket, spraying change all over the Oriental rug. Nickels, dimes, streetcar tokens and a rare bottle cap I had been saving softly distributed themselves in artistic patterns among the furniture legs. He laughed as he shook my sweaty hand. We both bent simultaneously to pick up my dropped effluvia. My sports coat hunched up over my shoulders, burying my ears deep in horsehair. Together we scavenged about under rich cordovan leather, behind carved-ebony claws holding cut-crystal orbs.

"By George, this is interesting," he said as he scooped up my Magic Tom Mix Good-Luck Charm with the embossed secret Tom Mix TM Bar password.

"Heh, heh . . . yeah . . ." I replied.

I tried to hide the bottle cap, but it was no use. Three times I dropped my rare collector's item before I finally got it back into my pocket.

"You're Shepherd, aren't you, son?" His voice was yeasty, deep; it bounced off the oil portrait.

"Yeah. Heh, heh . . ."

"Sit down, my boy. Care for some sherry?"

"Uh . . . yeah. Heh, heh . . . I really liked cherry pop. How did he know? He pulled a cloth cord on the wall. A minute later, the old guy who had let me in appeared in the door.

"You rang, sir?"

"Yes, Drew. Bring us some of the sherry, will you? Well, young man, it certainly is tiresome waiting for the womenfolk, isn't it?"

"Yeah. It sure is. Heh, heh. It sure is . . ."

"Say! . . ." He looked at me with great interest, his white brows arched, his magnificent teeth glowing healthily. "Aren't you one of the Pittsburgh Shepherds?"

"Uh . . ."

He continued: "The Pittsburgh *steel* Shepherds?"

I could feel, actually *hear*, my face getting beet red. The Pittsburgh STEEL Shepherds! All I knew about Pittsburgh was that the Pirates came from there, but I did have an uncle who worked in the 40-inch soaking pits at the steel mill. I couldn't see how Mr. Bigelow would know him.

"Well, yes . . . I guess so. I do have some relatives in steel."

He slapped his knee and laughed.

"By George, I thought you looked like old Googie! I haven't seen the old rascal since our class reunion at New Haven! The next time you see him, tell him Max

Bigelow said—now get this, he'll know what it means—
Bango!" He roared.

"Heh, heh. I sure will."

"Don't forget, boy. Bango!"

Over his shoulder, off in the middle distance, I saw a
maid moving back and forth along the immense table,
touching a glass, arranging a napkin. A huge grandfather
clock, seven feet tall, all brass and dark wood, ticked
quietly in the rich air.

The old guy shoved a silver tray under my nose and
smiled. Panicky, I reached for the thinnest, tiniest glass I
had ever seen. It looked like my Uncle Carl's eyecup,
only tinier. I had it for a brief instant between my
thumb and forefinger, its stem barely discernible. And
then, suddenly, it tipped over and the warm amber fluid
soaked into my best slacks, dripping down inside over
my kneecap and down my leg, to be absorbed by my
Argyles.

"Oops!" Mr. Bigelow bellowed. "Bad luck!" Immediately, the old guy was back with another glassful. I took
it and held it tight.

"Cheers!"

"What?"

"In your eye!"

"What?"

It was then that I think he began to suspect. He
sipped his drink and watched me narrowly as I raised my
glass to my mouth and drained it in a single gollop. A
raging bolt of fire streaked downward.

"Gaaahhhkkk!"

"What did you say, boy?"

". . . Gork!" My eyes watered, my throat burned. Deep in my stomach a pot began to boil. Never in my life had I had anything stronger than a fleeting sip of my Uncle Tom's homemade root beer.

Mr. Bigelow settled back in his deep leather armchair and for the first time really looked at me. It was then, inexplicably, that my sports coat began to glow in the dark. His beautifully cut muted mocha creation looked like no suit I had ever seen before. It was not a Cleveland Street pick-'em-off-the-pipe-rack special. Even I knew it. My father's only good suit was a kind of yellowish color with a tasty kelly-green plaid. Its lapels, high and sweeping, jutted out like the mainsails on a Spanish galleon. He always wore his lodge button stuck in the left sail, a pin the size of a nickel made in the shape of a Sacred Beaver. He belonged to the Royal Order of the Beaver, Dam 28. Mr. Bigelow wore no pins.

Stealthily, I tried to hide my left cuff link, which had somehow begun to send a shaft of purple light to the ceiling. No sooner had I gotten it under my electric-blue sleeve than the other one switched on even brighter. I pulled it out of sight and sat with both arms clamped behind me, my French cuffs crinkling. Then I noticed that my beautiful shoes were getting wider; the soles of which I was so proud had grown thicker and squeakier. I tried to hide my Argyles by tucking my bowling balls under the chair. Mr. Bigelow watched, but said nothing. Finally he called out:

245

"Daphne. Your . . . *date* is here." His voice had changed.

"Well, have fun," he said to me. "Don't stay out too late." He smiled, again that lemon twist that Daphne used, then rose and left the room.

Almost on cue, Daphne appeared atop the broad, sweeping balustrade and glided gracefully down the thick, carpeted stairs. I stood, my cuff links jangling, my shoes squeaking, the bottle cap in my pocket clanking loudly against my Tom Mix lucky charm, my enormous padded shoulders swinging back and forth. But I was not at a loss for words.

"Heh, heh . . . Hi, Daphne."

"So glad to see you."

"Yeah. Likewise."

"Well, shall we go?"

We moved from room to room, down the marble entrance hall and finally out onto the dark, amber-lit veranda.

"Dad said we could use the car."

"The car?"

A long black Cadillac gleamed like an ebony crypt in the driveway, the one I had half seen near school. A man in black darted out of the bushes and opened the back door with a sweep. Daphne stepped in. In my panic, I cracked my shin such a thump against the doorsill that my teeth rattled for an instant.

"Heh, heh . . . By George!" I hadn't lost my presence of mind.

I hobbled into the car, stumbled across a deep wall-to-wall rug and groped my way to the back seat, my leg throbbing dully. A thin trickle of blood oozed down my shin.

We waited in the drive. In the front seat, the man who had opened the door sat quietly. After what seemed like 20 minutes. Daphne finally came out with:

"Well?"

"Well, it sure is a nice night out." I was really sharp tonight.

The driver turned and said, "Where to?"

Daphne waited. The Cadillac waited. The driver waited. Fuzzily suspecting they were waiting for me, I took the plunge:

"Uh . . . the Orpheum."

The driver said, "The *Orpheum?*" with a rising inflection that was familiar. Many teachers had used it on me before, an effective oleo of dignity and scorn. Daphne, her voice calm, said quietly:

"Yes, Raymond. The Orpheum." The note of stainless-steel authority was one she did not use in Biology II. I had not seen this side of Daphne. It interested me.

Silently, the car began to roll. We wound through the trees, past the flower beds and out into the great night through the tunnel of green, past looming hedges, wrought-iron gates, antique lanterns, and finally into the street.

I flayed my jelly-like mind for something to say. Where was my agile whipcord brain? What had happened to my famed cool irony? Finally, I quipped:

"Boy, it sure is nice out."

"Yes, it is a lovely evening."

"It sure is. Boy."

A flash of inspiration percolated through the coffee grounds of my cranium: "Old Settlemeyer's really a gasser, isn't he? Boy!"

"He *is* . . . amusing."

I did not know till that moment how wide, how vast, car seats could be. Daphne was at least 30 yards out of field-goal range, perched miles away from me on the billowing dove-gray cushion we shared. Raymond, two and a half miles ahead of us, was obviously clearly out of earshot.

Dauntless, I wondered how she would react to a quick clinch. I watched her out of the corner of my eye to see whether there were any outward signs of passion yet. It was hard to tell at that distance. Finally, I decided once again to play it safe, a tendency that has cursed me all of my life.

We were now in the streetcar—hot-dog-stand-neon-sign belt. As the terrain became more and more jazzy, more familiar, my courage rose. I was just on the point of making a quick grab for her delicately turned ankle and risking the whole caper on one shot in the dark when we drew up before the Orpheum. Such was my frenzy that I was caught off guard and didn't notice that the car had stopped and Raymond was holding the door open for our descent back into the real world.

"Well, here we are," said Daphne pointedly.

Coming to, I stepped out of the limousine, cracking my good ankle heavily against the curb. Where I came

from, cars had running boards. Raymond, alert, shot
a hand out as I pitched forward, grabbing my left shoulder
pad in an iron grip like a quarterback about to throw a
60-yard pass. Of course, all he got was a handful of
the horsehair, excelsior and tiny bedsprings with which
my coat was equipped to give me the stylish Chicago
Bears lineman look that was so admired in the sophomore
class. A few threads snapped and gave, but I stood upright.

"Are you all right, sir?"

"I was just kiddin' around."

I playfully belted him in the ribs. He coughed slightly
and drew back, his eyes flat, opaque.

"Just havin' a little fun, Raymond."

He did not laugh.

Daphne joined me on the sidewalk under the brilliant
glare of the white lights of the friendly old Orpheum
marquee. The usual motley rabble that hung around the
Orpheum entranceway every night—to watch the girls go
in or just to look at the red-and-yellow posters displaying
sinister Japanese soldiers tying Merle Oberon to 500-
pound bombs—openly gawked at the black land yacht,
Daphne, and my electric-blue coat. Quickly I scanned
the crowd, hoping for at least one envious face. There
was none. I bought the tickets and we passed inside. Mr.
Woscowski, who had replaced Mr. Doppler as manager
after the infamous Orpheum gravy-boat riot of my youth;
took the two tickets, ripped them across and dropped
them in the slot with one motion. I tried to catch his eye

in order to let Daphne know how widely known I was, but he ignored me.

Into the blackness we went. Some of the more meaningful moments of my life had been spent in this dark, warm cocoon. The Orpheum had always seemed to me one of the greatest places in the world. With suave assurance I convoyed Daphne safely down the littered aisle, popcorn crunching underfoot, ankle-deep in candy wrappers, to my favorite row of seats in the left-hand section halfway down. We sat directly behind a couple who, if not engaged in actual copulation, were certainly doing a good impersonation of it. On the screen a 75-foot John Wayne glared stonily into the rolling hills.

Since I had seen the picture twice before, I hoarsely outlined the part we had missed into Daphne's fragrant, shell-like ear. But I got the distinct impression of a lack of concentration on her part. Ahead of us the two seats squeaked and groaned. The girl, if that's what she was, giggled briefly as they battled on. A masculine voice in the darkness ahead mingled with the sound track overriding it sharply:

"Aw, for Crissake, Nan, come on!"

"Stop it!"

The slap of flesh sharply striking flesh, followed by a burst of raucous laughter.

I became aware of a movement behind as a large knee crept up the back of my seat and rested on my right shoulder. It pushed forward, tilting my seat three or four inches nearer the combatants ahead. I turned and said politely into the darkness:

"Do you mind removing your knee?"

A blast of alcohol engulfed me.

"WHO'S GONNA MAKE ME, YOU SON OF A BITCH?"

Now, in the Orpheum under normal circumstances, this was a direct cue for action. For a moment I almost forgot myself. Fighting for control, however, I forced myself to ignore the outrage and said to Daphne through clenched teeth:

"John Wayne is sure good."

She said nothing. She was sitting bolt upright, a rare sight in the Orpheum, and seemed to be peering around in the darkness at the huddled figures that surrounded us.

"Who ya lookin' at, baby?" a merry-making steelworker asked bluntly. Another challenge.

Daphne, tilting her head gracefully, whispered into my ear:

"This is a very *interesting* place."

It had never occurred to me that the Orpheum was a very interesting place, at least not the way she put it.

"Yeah. It's great. Really great."

Somewhere far off to our right, someone unleashed a gigantic, resonant burp, after a prolonged rasping gurgle, a guy really dredging it up from the bottom. Scattered applause and laughter followed. From the balcony a shower of Cracker Jack drifted down over the center section, accompanied by three folded airplanes that danced briefly in silhouette over the Western prairies.

"Wouldja like some popcorn?" I asked.

251

"No, thank you."

"How 'bout a Coke?"

"Maybe later."

We sat numbly together in the rickety seats. Comparative calm reigned for half a reel or so, and then the final collapse of the evening began. During a tense moment on the screen—in dead silence as John Wayne waited for the attacking rustlers to come over the hill, the audience crouching forward in nervous anticipation, Daphne herself showing discernible signs of interest—a low rumbling began. At first I thought it was a DC-3 flying over on its way to Chicago. It got closer and closer, louder and louder. It seemed to come from all directions at once, a low bass thrumming. It grew in volume. In the dark, my palms turned to ice. Oh God no, not now!

My stomach was rumbling! It was a great joke in the family that when I missed supper, or a meal was late, the old gut would bang it out like an anvil. As the roaring gurgle sighed off into the distance like a freight train crossing a viaduct, the voice behind me, still on the muscle, barked out:

"Cut it out, ya slob!"

More cackles. Daphne cleared her throat.

"Excuse me," I said.

After all, I didn't want the Bigelows to think I wasn't well brought up. My gut settled down to its regular idle after the first clarion blast and continued muttering throughout the movie.

I had always taken the Orpheum for granted. All of it. But now I began to notice things that I had never been aware of. Somewhere off behind us there was a continual flushing of plumbing. I could hear the projector whirring, accompanied by the low-voiced, nonstop argument between the two operators. I hoped Daphne didn't notice. But she caught something else.

"Certainly smells funny here."

"What d'ya mean?"

"You don't notice?"

"Oh, yeah. Yeah. Sure."

After all these years coming to the Orpheum, how was it I had never before been aware of all those feet? I sat quietly, sorting out scent after scent, hoping desperately that Daphne didn't recognize most of them.

The picture neared the end. John Wayne told Charles Bickford, the cattle baron, how he'd have to move on 'cause he was the roamin' kind. I knew it was now or never. My fingers crept softly over my knee, over the armrest, poised in the dark for a moment and then dropped slowly over Daphne's exquisitely modeled hand. For a few seconds we sat unmoving; her fingers, cool and smooth, nestled in my sweaty palm. I stared straight ahead, afraid to break the spell. Even my stomach stopped rumbling out of respect for this magic moment. Ahead of us, the tangled couple had fallen into a comatose state, lulled perhaps by satiation or maybe by the tender sentiments of *Hearts Aflame at the Old Corral.* Thus we sat to the final frame, the last slanting rays of the Western sun outlining a lone rider galloping into the distance.

The lights came up. Unfastening our hands, we moved

together back up the aisle and out into the glare of the marquee. Welders, steam fitters, kids, old men wearing black hats pushed and shoved around us. The Cadillac waited. Raymond at the wheel. Daphne said the first thing either of us had uttered for hours, it seemed:

"That was certainly a very interesting place. I'm really glad you brought me to it. Do you come here often?"

"Nah. I just thought you might find it interesting."

"Well, it certainly was."

We were back inside the chariot. Already its rich dove-gray aroma seemed homey and familiar to me. I was about to instruct Raymond to wheel us down to the old Red Rooster when Daphne said in a small voice:

"It's certainly late, isn't it? I had no idea how late it was."

Raymond, without a word, turned his battleship against the traffic and we headed back toward the North Side. For a few moments nothing was said, as the limousine hummed silently along. The heady excitement of social triumph surged through me. Stealthily my hand crept like a predatory spider over the soft mohair, closer and closer to Daphne, as I whistled a few snatches from the Hohman High Victory Song. Raymond tooled on, coolly, discreetly, as the trees grew higher, the privet hedges appeared and the neon signs receded.

Closer and closer. We touched! For a single quivering instant, and then quietly she drew her hand away, laying it in her mysterious lap.

"Did you finish that caterpillar drawing?" she asked.

"Caterpillar drawing?"

"In lab."

"Oh, yes. You can copy it Monday."

We rode on in silence. I groped frantically for some feeble straw, some last bit of flotsam to cling to, to keep the conversation going. It was no use.

"I sort of like Mr. Settlemeyer," she said finally.

"He's all right, I guess."

We pulled in the drive, up to the veranda and stopped. Raymond whipped the door open. This time I knew how to get out. Daphne took my hand and shook it, the second time it had happened in the same night!

"I've had a very lovely time, and I want to thank you."

"I had a great time, too. It sure was great."

"Raymond would be glad to drive you home."

"Oh, no, I'll walk. I live just a few blocks over, on Harrison," I lied spectacularly.

"Well, see you in class. Good night."

She was gone.

"Sure you don't want a ride, Bud?" Raymond had changed.

Without a word, I turned and walked down the long curving asphalt drive between the flower beds, under the trees, past the stone sundial, the iron gates, the white sign that read BIGELOW, out into the night, walked in my electric-blue sports coat, my hated, rotten, crummy electric-blue sports coat, its padding squishing and banging against my shoulder blades, its hem flapping against my knees, walked with my long, fluttering tinfoil noose with its monster snail crawling up and down—my despised, ridiculous tie—walked in my booby, pleated, sacky clown

255

pants, walked in my Tony-Martin-collared, French-cuffed, miserable, jazzy shirt. Walked and walked.

I had struck out. My old man had struck out. My mother had struck out. Even my kid brother had struck out. I sailed my Tom Mix lucky charm off across the street toward a delicate, lacy gazebo and walked on, mile after mile, through leafy streets, under catalpa trees, eventually past lurking pool halls, taverns, junk yards, used-car lots. I never knew it was so far to the North Side. Finally I walked under the Bull Durham sign, past the Bluebird, up the back steps, through the screen door and into the kitchen. It was then I remembered for the first time that the invitation to the spring ball was still in my pocket.

I breathed in the aroma of red cabbage, spilled ketchup, fermenting Brillo pads, my mother's Chinese-red chenille bathrobe. Opening the refrigerator, I peered into the yellow, fragrant interior. A dish of peas from last week, a meatball with a bite out of it, what was left of a baked ham, a plastic container with some pickled beets. Home. Smelly home.

Grabbing the meatball, I stuffed it in my mouth, washing it down with milk from the bottle, and was about to rip off a piece of ham when the kitchen light blasted on. Her hair in curlers, her bathrobe hanging limply, my mother beamed sleepily.

"Did you have a good time?"

"Sure did."

"Were you nice to them?"

"Yep."

"Well, that's nice. I don't want them to think you aren't well brought up. Well, hurry to bed."

"OK. Night."

I finished the food, snapped off the light, stumbled through the dark into my bedroom, removed my repulsive sports coat and my pleated slacks—smelling faintly of sherry—and threw them in the corner next to my baseball bats. I sat on the edge of my bed in the dark. A sparrow rustled under the eaves outside the window. In the next room my kid brother muttered in his sleep. The sink burped moodily. The refrigerator chugged and squeaked. I thought briefly of that long table, with all the crystal and the maid touching things here and there. I wondered idly if Esther Jane Alberry had gotten her invitation to the spring ball yet. Then I lay back on my lumpy mattress and finally fell asleep, but not without a struggle.

THE RETURN OF THE
SMILING WIMPY DOLL

"Kongratulations upon buying such a fine procuring our very fine patented (Pend.) products! You have choosed wisely upon devices. The guarante which accompanies herein is unquestionably good for one year or less. If fuse is not twisted? Note base of green color is not easily found to be crackable. To operate correctfully merely plug into standard U.S. (A.C.) two pronged electrics (110 V.). Immediately your Deluxe Yule A-Go-Go Tuneful Musical Revolving Puncture-Proof Table-Model Aluminum Xmas Tree should begins function. (Deluxe Model 2-A is capable of being folds. If excessive care is observed. This provide storage.)"

I reread the directions, which must contain somewhere a clue to the technical trouble I was experiencing with my sparkling little Japanese-made aluminum beauty, a triumph of modern science over the tuneless, nonreusable, old-fashioned Christmas tree of yesteryear. The only trouble was, the damn thing squatted there dark, mute and unrevolving in the middle of my winter-streaked picture window overlooking my beloved wasteland of Manhattan, even though I had taken every precaution to make sure it was plugged into the correct electrics. Maybe my Yule A-Go-Go is polarized, I thought, with my usual technical know-how, on which I pride myself as an ex-GI.

Dropping to my knees, I crawled laboriously behind my Danish Folding Swing-A-Ding Coucherama, inching forward toward the only electrical outlet that my entire high-rent, three-and-a-half-room apartment supported. I plunged my hand into the giant rat's nest of three-way, five-way, nine-way extensions and plugs, by dint of which I managed to squeeze out enough electricity from my one outlet to run my entire life. From somewhere in the distance, deep in some murky air shaft, came the faint strains of recorded Christmas music. I jiggled the plugs, reversed the green one from my Yule A-Go-Go and crabbed backward from behind the couch.

Nothing. Returning to the tree, I picked it up and examined it from all sides in the gray light that filtered in from what passes for a winter sun in the big city. There were no knobs, no switches, no unseemly mechanistic protuberances. Aha! Again my brilliant technical mind leaped in excitement as I spotted on the underside of the Christmas-green polyethylene base what appeared to be the head of an embedded fuse. Quickly I scanned again the thinner-than-tissue-paper sheet of instructions. A single phrase leaped out at me: "If fuse is not twisted?" Do they mean to *twist* the fuse or *not* to twist the fuse? Since my Yule A-Go-Go wasn't yet playing carols and suffusing my apartment with a festive aura of soft Christmas lighting the way the ad said it would, I deduced that they must mean to *twist* the fuse.

Squinting closely at the base, I observed that the fuse was recessed well below the surface. It would require more than my fingernails to do the job. In a frenzy of creativity, I rushed out into my kitchen, where I kept my meager supply of tools, fished out my dime-store pliers and reurned to the fray. As I grasped the base firmly in one hand, the pliers in the other chomped solidly onto the head of the fuse. I gave it a smooth and clean twist.

For a single instant I felt the Christmas tree stir under my grasp, its tiny red, yellow, blue and green lights flaring brightly. The high, thin notes of "I'm dreaming of a white Christmas" bounced off the ceiling. Then a dull, roaring sensation boomed up my arm, crashed into my shoulder, down my spine, hovered for a moment in my pelvic region and then whinged out through my other arm. For a moment, I stood frozen; then I toppled through a cloud of billowing smoke—striking my head smartly against the arm of my burnt-orange Naugahyde Barcalounger—and lay for a full minute, during which I had the clear impression of being on a skiing trip in the Alps, which is rather odd, since I am resolutely anti skiing. Tentatively, my mind gradually groped back into focus and I knew the worst. I had just voided another guarantee.

I crawled to my feet, my silken dressing gown still smoldering slightly, and staggered over to the couch. I sat down heavily, flicking my wrists, attempting to restore some circulation. It was a little early in the morning for shock therapy, I reflected. Christmas decorations lay scattered about me. Absent-mindedly, I examined a plastic bag containing two sprigs of neoprene mistletoe. In red, Christmasy lettering, PLASTOKISS splashed across the gay bagging. Well, at least you don't have to plug this stuff in, I mused.

Little did I realize that this fiasco was but a prelude to an electrifying pre-Christmas trauma that would set the tone for the entire yuletide fortnight. Wisps of blue-gray electrical smoke eddied about my bookshelves. The shock had given me a more than moderately nasty headache, which, piled on top of my usual Saturday-morning hangover, should have been enough hint of impending events. But we live from moment to moment, rarely perceiving the vaster plans that contrive to undo us.

The doorbell rang. My mind, slowed by its unexpected jolt of Con Ed juice, at first did not respond. It rang again. Finally, I heard a disembodied voice that I dimly recognized as mine call out:

"What do you want?"

From beyond the door, I heard the surly, guttural tones of the doorman: "A package."

A package? Instantly the cobwebs fled. There is nothing that brings the roses to the cheeks of a man quicker than to announce he is receiving a package. Leaping to my feet, I lurched forward, barking my shins against my free-form coffee table, and limped to the door, oblivious of the thin crimson trail of blood I left behind me.

LIFE—THE COMPLETE CEREAL. Sweat poured down my

brow as I read the green block letters printed on the huge, lumpy, battered cardboard carton as I struggled to drag it over the sill of my apartment door. Slowly I inched the monster burden over my $700-a-yard, mocha-shaded wall-to-wall carpeting and into the living room, my Sulka dressing gown sopping wet with honest perspiration. Even the monogram drooped.

Painfully, I toppled the hulking mass end upward, hearing from inside a muffled clinking and clattering, a tinkling, rolling, sifting, grating mélange of sound from within the battered carton. Even as I eased myself down into my magnificent alligatorskin Pakistani sling chair to rub my shattered shin, which was now beginning to throb, the box continued to emit muted noises, like sand filtering down through a mess of broken Christmas-tree ornaments. From deep inside came the low whir of a spring suddenly uncoiling. It stopped, ticked twice and was silent. Somehow, that spring and the sound it made were vaguely familiar. Then began a faint, derisive quacking, as of some demented duck calling to its lascivious mate. Instinctively, I struck out at the carton with my clenched fist. The duck quacked once again and the giant carton lapsed into an ominous silence. Only the sound of distant sirens, keeping the citizenry at bay, drifted in from the outside world.

I knew that damn duck! Which is not an easy fact to accept before lunch. Awkwardly, I struggled out of my chair and stood looking down at my prize. For the first time, I noticed that there was an envelope taped on the top. It was addressed to me, hand-written in a familiar script:

> Merry Christmas. I was cleaning out the basement the other day and I came across all kinds of junk you had when you were little. I figured rather than throw it out, I'd send it on to you. A lot of it is still good and you might want to play with it, especially the Kangaroo Spring-Shus that Aunt Min gave you for Christmas.
>
> Love,
> Mom

With an involuntary groan, I plumped down on my rickety camel-saddle seat and read the letter again, finally letting it fall to the floor between my feet. Seven tons of kid effluvia! What a master stroke of sadistic Christmas gift giving! Already my apartment was loaded to the gunnels with *grown-up* mementos—my complete library of first-edition *Peanuts* paperbacks, my matched set of souvenir pillows from 37 Army camps west of the Mississippi, my matchless, nationally known collection of rare swizzle sticks, all personally earned. My life was already overflowing. And now this! I thought briefly of throwing the whole mess down the air shaft.

Then, from deep inside the box came another sound, a faint honking, as of some ancient flivver caught in a long-forgotten traffic jam. It stopped. Maybe it was the duck, maybe the horn, maybe Christmas itself; but I found myself rising slowly from the camel seat, picking

up my pair of shears and standing over the vast carton.
From some remote apartment came the unmistakable
beat of that new smash Christmas hit *The King Wences-
laus Rock* by the Bullwhip Four. Taking a deep breath,
I plunged the shears into the top of the box. There
was no turning back. As I sawed away, I began to be
conscious of a rising twinge of apprehension. What was
in this box? After all, as a kid, I had had a lot of things
in my possession at one time or another that I would
not want my mother to know about. Furthermore, it
came as a somewhat nasty shock that this stuff was still
in existence.

Finally, the shears chewed through the last strand of
baling wire and the top of the battered receptacle stood
ready for the final assault. Unflinching, I grasped the
flaps and ripped. Instantly, an odd, indefinable odor rose
from the muddled moil: musty, basementy, a slight touch
of rust. I think I detected even a bit of residual ancient
sweat mixed with other scents so subtle and ephemeral
as to be unclassifiable.

Inside the cover, my mother had crumpled large sec-
tions of the editorial page and want-ad columns from
an old copy of the *Chicago Tribune* that she had picked
up, probably, from a pile of old newspapers in the basement. One faded headline read: "B-24 SQUADRON HITS
SICILY IN DAYLIGHT RAID; REPORT SUCCESS; THREE PLANES
LOST." The crumpled panels of a comic strip caught my
eye. I smoothed it out and once again was face to face
with Harold Teen. He was trying to get Lillums, his
little lettuce leaf, to go to Pop Jenks' Sugar Bowl with

him. Then Beezie Jenks said something that will be forever lost, since that part of the strip was ripped away. I noticed that Terry had not made second lieutenant yet but was still a struggling air cadet. Ruthlessly, I crumpled the papers, tossed them aside and peered down into the gloomy morass within the box. It was worse than I thought. A rich, moldering compost heap lay like some archaeological treasure-trove before me. For a fleeting instant, I felt like King Tut would feel if he came back and somebody insisted he take a tour through the Egyptian section of the Museum of Natural History to look at all his junk in the glass cases.

Gingerly, I reached down into this sorry mess of pottage—I must admit, with a certain amount of uneasiness, because there was no telling what was in there, and I've always been worried about getting bitten by things. Warily I grasped a round, furry projection that barely topped the surface of this sea of trivia and slowly began to pull from the rubble a battered, fuzzy, brownish, truncated form, which, as it began to emerge from the wreckage, I recognized with growing horror. Great Scott! There, staring insidiously up at me, hanging from my fingers by one ear, was something from so far gone in my dim past that at first I thought this was just some nasty trick of my mother's. But no, I knew it was mine.

I don't know how to say this, but there, right in my apartment in midtown Manhattan, surrounded by my paperbacks of Kafka, Nietzsche and Rona Jaffe, was—please don't think too harshly of me—my Teddy bear. Yes, I confess it. There was a period in my life when I would no sooner have gone to bed without Brownie than I would have thought of saying bad things about Santa Claus. And there he was, looking up at me, one black button eye hanging loose, the other peering right through me with the steadfast, baleful glare of one who knew me when and knew me all too well. And clinging to him, so help me, was the faint but unmistakable aroma of what is euphemistically called baby "urps"— vague remains of ancient Pablum, petrified oatmeal and insinuating touches of Fletcher's Castoria.

I held Brownie out at arm's length before me. He dangled, revolving slowly in the ambient air—immutable, imperishable, eternally cuddly, wanting only to comfort me in the dark hours of slumber. Discreetly, I turned his good eye away from me, since he seemed to be trying to tell me something, laid him down on the sofa and wandered over to the window to stare for a long, gloomy moment out over the teeming city. If the word ever got out in certain circles that my pad housed a Teddy bear named Brownie, it would do me no good at all. The mere fact that I had ever *owned* a Teddy bear would have been enough in some quarters!

Bracing myself with a drink, I returned to the box, Taking a little more care this time to guard against undue shock. I slowly withdrew from the entanglement a flat, stuffed, cutout figure made of colored oilcloth. It stood approximately 12 inches high. For a long moment, this strange apparition and I confronted each other without a spark of recognition. Dusty, a bit faded, a little round oilcloth man wearing a derby and sporting a ragged mustache and a potbelly, he smiled enigmatically over my shoulder toward the kitchen. Somehow he looked familiar, and yet. . . . Then, from some far-off rubbish heap of memory, I heard a voice, a cracked, comical voice on the radio, asking, beseeching, demanding, wheedling, whimpering for more hamburgers. My God! Hurray! It's my Wimpy doll!

It will surprise many historians to learn that at one point in American history there was actually a Popeye radio program. Popeye, Olive and Castor Oyl, Ham Gravy, Wimpy and the whole crowd came into the living room every day. They offered you a choice of a Wimpy doll, a Popeye doll, an Olive Oyl doll or an Alice the Goon doll if you ate enough soup and sent in the labels. We were a canned-soup family, so there was no problem collecting enough labels, but I was probably the only kid in the United States who didn't order a Popeye doll; I went for Wimpy, a down-at-the-heels moocher who lived only to stuff his gut with hamburgers. I identified with him; and I'll never forget the day my Wimpy doll arrived. He immediately outranked Brownie; and for one hectic era, I was one of the very few Americans who went to bed every night with a guy wearing a derby and smoking a cigar. I must admit I was glad to see the old freeloader again. His oilcloth was a little seedy; the stuffing was edging out of his frock coat, but somehow that was as it should be for Wimpy. Carefully, I laid him alongside his old rival and returned to the hustings.

A thin leatherette strap caught my eye and carefully,

so as not to break any of these precious artifacts, I dragged forth a strange, dusty, dangling black object covered with snaps and buckles and exuding the heady aroma of musty sheepskin. Faint silver letters could be seen through the basement patina of grime. Dipping a finger in my drink, I carefully wiped off the grease and dirt. B-U—one letter was missing—K—another missing letter—O-G-E. . . . Bless my buttons! My genuine Buck Rogers Space Helmet! For intergalactic flight. With sheepskin lining and—uh-oh, don't tell me! My old lady's lost them or thrown them out! I hurriedly scrabbled through the tangled mess and, with a great sigh of relief, pulled out my precious space goggles. Oh, wow! Their scratched, yellowed plastic lenses were curling at the edges, but I reverently pulled them down over my head and snapped them into place—after first carefully shaking out three dead cockroaches and an elderly retired moth. I tugged at the ear flaps of my space helmet, squeezing it down over my cranium, marveling at how it had shrunk. Finally, I snapped the chin strap shut and rushed into my bedroom to admire myself in the mirror, as I had done so many times in the past. Ah, yes, the same intrepid traveler to the 25th Century, the fearless, flinty-red protector of the beauteous Wilma, old Dr. Huer's trusted friend, stared back out at me. But there was one thing missing.

Instantly, I was back at the box—and, sure enough, there it was, a little rusty, a little pock-marked, but still excitingly dangerous-looking. Made of imitation blue steel, it was my faithful Flash Gordon Zap Gun, the same gun that had destroyed Ming the Merciless with its deadly Disintegrator Rays. I leveled it at my Black Forest Persian Water Clock and pulled the trigger: Twa-aaannng! The achingly familiar sound of the deadly rays with which I had gunned down my kid brother, disintegrated Flick, Kissel and Schwartz thousands of times over echoed weakly in the room. The scratchy sheepskin tickled my ears the way it had so often in the past. This helmet and I had been through hell together—not to mention giant snowstorms through which I had burrowed, trusty goggles protecting my eyes, as I pretended that I was on a space flight to Venus, Buck Rogers Space Rockets strapped to my back, on my way to trap the vile Black Barney, who was now in league with Zog, evil master of the Swamp Planet, to subjugate the entire known universe.

Faintly, through the leatherette, the sounds of the *1812 Overture* from my stereo-FM tuner reminded me of one of the bloodiest battles I had ever fought in my kidhood. It directly involved the honor and reputation of my idol Buck Rogers. Without provocation and entirely without grounds, Schwartz had alleged that Flash Gordon could take Buck Rogers any day and that if it wasn't for Flash, Ming the Merciless of the planet Mongo would have us all in his clutches. This slander could not be brooked by any Buck Rogers fan, so we mixed it up under Schwartz' front porch for the better part of an hour, rolling in the dirt, tearing our shirts, banging each other's heads on the rocks, sweating and crying. But he didn't convince me and I didn't convince him. In any case, it was good to have this helmet back. You never know when it might come in handy.

I knew that somewhere in that pile of kid junk there must be the Buck Rogers Spaceship that I had gotten from the Buck Rogers radio program. It was made of lead and attached to a long string, which you were supposed to tie to a chandelier; given the proper shove, the spaceship would then twirl around the room, making a high, whistling sound. Which it did, until one night when my old man got it in the eye in the dark and ripped it down, tearing half the chandelier off the ceiling.

Reverently, I removed my helmet and goggles, laid aside my zap gun and reached once again into the grab bag. After fumbling around for a moment or two, I felt a round metallic object, which I at first thought was my beloved Mickey Mouse watch, a beautiful timepiece whose dapper yellow gloves occasionally pointed to more or less the correct time. But it wasn't. Corroded, its gilt finish peeling, it was the size of a watch, but beneath its glass top I could see the number 227.4. I scraped off some of the grime and read the embossed inscription—OFFICIAL JACK ARMSTRONG WHEATIES PEDOM-ETER.

From out of the wind tunnel of my mind, a commanding voice dramatically intoned: "Fellas and gals, with the Official Jack Armstrong Pedometer, you can tell just how far you walk every day, how far it is to school, how many miles it is to the store or the scout meeting. You'll never be lost if you wear your Jack Armstrong

Pedometer at all times. For just one Wheaties boxtop and twenty-five cents mailed to Jack Armstrong in care of this station. . . ." This was an important find. I examined the pedometer closely, ticking the counter lever with my thumb. It still worked. It still made that telltale click at each revolution. I remembered great herds of kids wearing corduroy knickers drifting schoolward through the boondocks, clicking as they went. The whole neighborhood sounded like an enormous flock of crickets, day and night, as kids measured how far it was to everywhere. I could still see the funny look on Miss Shields' face as, one day in fourth grade, I got up, on direct orders, to go to the blackboard to demonstrate my grasp of the multiplication table.

"What's that clicking?" asked Miss Shields.

"I'm measuring how far it is from my seat to the board," I said.

"Give me that," is all she said as she stuck the eighth pedometer of the day in her bottom drawer.

Pulling up my pajamas, I strapped the pedometer to my right knee, got up and carefully paced the distance to my bar, returned to my seat and took a reading. Hasty calculations revealed that six martinis would result in traveling one twelfth of a mile. Happy as a clam, I dug back into the box and unsuspectingly unearthed a shadowy horror out of my past that caused me to rock back in my chair in a wave of terror. My God! The evidence still exists! The crime had lain dormant in the back of my mind for years, gnawing at my conscience like some dry rot in the foundations of a haunted house.

Furtively, I examined my find, shielding it in my hand so that if by remote chance there were onlookers, they would not see the incriminating cellophane envelope that I held. That old sick nausea of fear of discovery, of the unmasking of my calumny, the exposure of my rottenness, hit me again. I am not proud of what I had done, but I was young and unformed. Youth is always immoral, but if I had it to do over again, I know I would do the right thing. I held it up to the light, and there they were within the envelope—yellow and green, light blue, triangular shaped, the collection of "Rare exotic hard-to-find Foreign stamps," which, in a headstrong moment of criminality, I had once sent away for—on approval. On approval meant you sent them your dime *after* you got the stamps. I do not have to tell you that I not only never sent in the dime, I never intended to. I remember the letter that came from Kansas City a month later, threatening my father with jail and me with a criminal record that would last throughout my life if I didn't ante up. I almost passed out when I read that; and after carefully burning it in the furnace, I decided I'd better pay. But I never did. I never heard from them again, although for years I had fleeting impressions of men in dark coats and Homburgs shadowing me wherever I went.

I tucked the stamp collection well back under the middle sofa cushion and moodily sipped my drink. Maybe that was the first misstep, I thought. Maybe if I had paid for those stamps, I could have marched through life clear-eyed, clean, honest, straight to the

White House. I'll bet Lyndon Johnson paid for *his* stamps! On second thought, however. . . .

It was with an effort that I returned to my investigation, fishing up next a collection of thin sheets of paper bound together with a crusty old rubber band that broke in my hand immediately, spilling the crinkly slips out over the floor. Cockamamies! I had unearthed some unused gems from the precious collection that I had bought over the years at Old Man Pulaski's. He really hated the times when we would come in to buy these tissue-paper tattoos that dissolved in water.

"All right, you kids, I ain't got no time for foolin' around. Either ya want pictures or ya don't."

Schwartz, Flick, Kissel and I, peering in through his glass case, would finally, after great soul-searching, decide on which magnificent artistic views of Old Faithful we wanted. I picked up from the floor a cockamamie showing a Marine in a green helmet sticking a bayonet into the thorax of a bright-yellow Jap soldier. A great fountain of crimson blood squirted out over the M-1. The Jap's eyes were slanted evilly, his mouth contorted as he hurled an Oriental obscenity at the square-jawed Marine. The caption read: "GUNG HO!" It was a beautiful picture, and I remember the day I bought it, my mother wouldn't let me put it on.

Here was my chance. I licked the ancient decal, tasting the old familiar glue flavor that I knew would not leave my mouth for a month, and meticulously smoothed the soggy cockamamie onto the back of my left hand, blowing on it expertly, as I had done so often in the past, to dry it off. Now for the delicate part. With the skill of a surgeon, I slowly peeled off the moist backing. There, in four beautiful colors on my left hand, was as magnificent a representation as I have ever seen of a Jap corporal going to his just rewards. I wondered what the gang at the office would say to me *now?* I knew that I would be the envy of all eyes and that it would especially impress the typing pool. I held my hand out admiringly, knowing that if I didn't wash my hands, I could keep it intact for at least a month.

By now, I must admit, I had been sucked bodily into this sobering and edifying dissection of my yeasty formative years. Old excitements and cravings, fugitive passions and desires crowded in upon me. With gusto, I drained off what remained of my bloody charlie and prepared to push on through the undergrowth of my childhood, little realizing the pitfalls and traps, the traumas that lay ahead.

My cockamamie had hardly dried when I found myself holding in my hand as sinister an object as I had ever owned, an object with a history of the sort that is rarely whispered in mixed company and that could and did make strong men weep. It was a penknife, but a penknife with a difference. Shaped like a lady's leg, no less—a lady's leg wearing a chromium-plated high-heeled shoe. The mother-of-pearl calf bulged enticingly and tapered off just above the knee. It carried two blades: one for ordinary cutting, the other for snipping off the butt ends of long black cigars. As I inspected it, the vision of an early but decisive humiliation sprang out from the knife directly into my consciousness.

My knees cracking warningly as I arose, I carried the grizzled weapon to the window. Holding it at the proper angle as I had done in the past, I looked for the silver shield embedded in the mother-of-pearl calf. Ah, yes, it was still there. I raised the knife to eye level, peering deep into the tiny hole in the shield, upward at the watery sun. There she was. My old paramour, who had contributed to many a sweaty evening and feverish dream, her grass skirt provocatively parted at mid-thigh, her roguish gypsy eyes glowing as brightly as ever, her ample and bare bazooms still in full, magnificent, flesh-colored bloom. She was the lady who had caused my disgrace and eventual court-martial from the Moose Patrol, Troop 41, Boy Scouts of America.

For months I had whined and cajoled, trying to pry out of my parents the price of an official Boy Scout knife. No one in our troop had a complete uniform. Some wore only khaki knickers; others sported only the broad-brimmed campaign hat; one or two had just a canteen; I owned only my purple neckerchief with the gold letters B.S.A. I wanted a knife to hang from my belt, like Flick had. My Uncle Carl, who spent the entire Depression playing his banjo and going in and out of poolrooms, hearing of my burning desire, one day fulfilled my wish. I distinctly recall the conversation. He wasn't wearing his false teeth that day, but he did have on his straw hat.

"I hear ya want a knife."

278

"Yeah."

"How would ya like this knife?" He fished out of his pocket the lady's leg in question.

"WOW!"

"Wait'll they see that at the Scout troop. That's better than any old Boy Scout knife," said Uncle Carl.

I held it in my hand for the first time. He bent over and whispered into my ear, his beery breath enveloping me in warmth and suds. "Look into that hole on the side. And don't tell your mother." That was the beginning. The next week, she was an instant smash hit at Troop 41's meeting. And two weeks later, I was drummed out in disgrace when Mr. Gordon got wind of what the Moose Patrol was cackling about.

I put my trusty knife into the pocket of my dressing gown and returned to the fray. An angry gust of December wind rattled my window as I wallowed among Christmases past, days of Ovaltine and morning-glories. I found myself holding a singular object that at first I did not recognize. In fact, it was so grotesque that it was hard to believe that the human mind could conceive of such a surrealistic *object d'art*—a gently curved, warted, plastic, winged golden pickle, imprinted with the cabalistic symbol "57." The number had a curiously familiar ring: 57 what? Operative 57? No, that didn't sound right. And why the pickle? Then it hit me. Heinz' 57 Varieties! Sponsored by the pickle company, Colonel Roscoe Turner and his famous Flying Corps, of which I was a fully licensed and qualified member, had appeared in a comic strip that ran under *Tillie the Toiler* back in

279

the days when Jiggs was hitting the corned beef and cabbage hard and Maggie was hitting Jiggs even harder. Turner's creased, intrepid face with the dashing Errol Flynn mustache had been the very embodiment of flying. His only passenger was a lion cub named Gilmore. I pinned the wings over my left breast and decided to have an extra shot of catsup with my hamburger that night, for old time's sake. There was a time when I devoutly believed that when I grew up, I would not only be a pilot but would own several pairs of beautifully tailored, whipcord pilot-type riding breeches. With puttees. Here I am, grown up as much as I'll ever be, and all I've got are a couple of pairs of baggy Bermuda shorts, and I don't even know where I could lay my hands on as much as a single puttee if I had to. They don't even *name* guys Roscoe anymore. He did more for the canned-soup and piccalilli industries than Billy Graham has done for evangelism.

The next 15 minutes I spent happily working the plunger on my Captain Midnight Ovaltine Shake-Up Mug, which I immediately saw would be handy in whipping up a batch of gibsons. I next blew several high, piercing blasts from my Captain Midnight Three-Way Mystic Dog Whistle, causing 17 mutts in apartments as far as two blocks away to howl and bark frantically as I communicated to them in Captain Midnight's secret code, the same code that I had used to send secret messages across the back yards and alleys to Flick and Kissel.

Unexpectedly, I then ran across a veritable fortune

in unrealized assets. Here, for years, I had been moderately wealthy and did not know it. I discovered seven—
that's right, *seven*—unredeemed Good Humor Lucky
Sticks, each good for one free Good Humor bar any
time I cared to cash them in. I could not figure how I
had let them go by the boards when I was a kid; but
then it slowly came back to me—the summer I had
hoarded them for my old age. I had read a story in a
comic book about an old man who didn't save when
he was a kid and now was reduced to begging on street
corners. The moral was to Save For A Rainy Day. It
scared me so much that I began to lay away uncashed
pop bottles, Lucky Sticks and slugs for free games on the
pinball machine. Vestiges of chocolate syrup remained
on the valuable premiums. I wondered briefly whether
I could cash the whole lot in with Emile, the bartender
at the Existentialiste du Morte, for an Irish coffee.

With moist eyes, I riffled through my prized collection
of Fleer's bubble-gum cards, illustrating great moments
in American history. There was good old Washington
still crossing the Delaware, Paul Revere galloping over
the countryside on a green horse, Abraham Lincoln making a speech. Dog-eared, thumbed, well worn and
faithful, my collection—one of the world's most valuable
of its kind—was completely intact. As I glanced at them,
my jaw hinges ached dully from countless pounds of
obscenely pink bubble gum that I had pulverized to
get these cards. One card, in particular, told a story.
It showed Robert Fulton waving a flag from the deck
of his steamship. That card had cost me four fillings

in one chomp of the gum; the sickening crunch of a mouthful of silver as the bubble gum did its deadly work is a feeling not soon to be forgotten.

The next item plunged me into such a funk as to necessitate an immediate trip to the sideboard for two fingers of the straight stuff. At first glance, it was a supremely innocent artifact. But to me, who lived through it, who suffered with it and was irrevocably scarred for life because of it, it was far more than a ten-cent package of nasturtium seeds. I looked at the brilliantly colored picture of gigantic prize-winning blossoms shown on the slender envelope of rattling seeds. It all came back —that grim week long ago that began with such high hopes and that ended in a black despair that had forever made me quail at the word "salesmanship."

Miss Shields that spring had enlisted us to sell seeds in the neighborhood in order to buy a set of World Books for the Warren G. Harding School. Her stirring, impassioned speech—exhorting us to get out and sell the seeds to "all your friends and neighbors who are waiting for you to deliver them"—had stirred me to sign up for a whole box of 12 envelopes. I ran all the way home, eager to hit the trail. My first jaunty knock was on the door of the gray house by the corner. A haggard, sleepy lady peered out of the darkness at me."

"What d'ya want?"

"Uh—d'ya want to buy any seeds?"

"Any what?"

"Seeds. I have marigolds, pansies, hollyhocks. . . ."

"*Seeds!*" The lady's red eyes glared out at me.

". . . Nasturtiums, morning-glories."

The door slammed shut. Miss Shields had not mentioned this possibility. At the next house, a large brown dog, closely related to the jaguar, chased me around the garage four times before I made it over the fence. Next door, a lady holding four babies and surrounded by a moiling thicket of wailing urchins peered dimly out at me, shaking her head silently.

House after house it went like this, until finally, at the end of four miles of humiliating defeat, I emerged a bent, stooped, tiny, wizened, nine year old Willy Loman —footsore and weary, without so much as a single seed sold. Finally, weeks later, various aunts paid for my stock, but I was left with this last unsold package of nasturtiums.

As that old sensation of self-pity overwhelmed me, my knuckles ached once again from knocking on unyielding doors as I stared through misty eyes at those brilliant nasturtiums. For some reason, I found myself wondering whether the seeds would actually grow and what they would produce if they did. I have heard that ancient grains of wheat taken from the tombs of Pharaohs have been made to sprout and prosper. Tenderly, I placed my remaining stock of seeds next to Wimpy. For a moment, I thought perhaps I might go out this afternoon, knock on a few apartment doors on my floor and maybe make a sale. But then the old fear took over and I knew I couldn't do it.

Right on the heels of the nasturtiums, as if by evil design, I came across a mint-condition flat-white can of

White Cloverine Brand Salve, another relic of my ill-fated career as a boy salesman. The ad in the comic book had read: "Kids! YOU may be the one to win this beautiful SHETLAND PONY! He will be awarded, along with thousands of other prizes, to winners in our big Sales Sweepstakes. Just help distribute to your friends and neighbors that old family stand-by White Cloverine Brand Salve." It pictured a smiling, freckle-faced, red-headed kid holding the reins of a brown-and-white Shetland. I clipped the coupon. God only knows what horrors would have descended on the household if I *had* won a pony.

Shortly thereafter, an enormous case full of White Cloverine Brand Salve arrived, and another trial by fire began. Once again, I was tested and found wanting. After 17 giant suppertime fights, and after I had sold only three cans of salve—one to my mother, one to Mrs. Kissel and one to me—my father wrapped the whole thing up and sent it back to the Cloverine people, hollering: "LET THE BASTARDS SUE! THEY CAN'T GET BLOOD OUT OF A ROCK! IF YOU EVER SEND ANOTHER DAMN COUPON IN, YOU WON'T SIT DOWN FOR A MONTH!" That ended that, technically, but nothing had ever sealed the ugly gash in my soul.

Next came my battered, rainbow-tinted Official Tournament Model Duncan Yo-Yo, its paint worn smoothly away along the groove from endless hours of Walking the Dog, its string knotted and blackened, trailing off into the mass of memorabilia. I pulled and tugged at it.

Something was attached to it. Out of the depths it came like a struggling freshwater catfish, glinting dully in the faint gray light of my apartment. I held it up, suspended from the yo-yo string, to examine it. Slowly spinning before my eyes was one of the true treasures of my youth, my Melvin Purvis G-Man Badge. I searched quickly and discovered, still intact and ready for action, its matching set of Melvin Purvis G-Man Escape-Proof Handcuffs, just like the ones John Dillinger had slipped out of so many times. I knew that somewhere down in the tangle must be my Melvin Purvis G-Man Book of Instructions on HOW TO STOP CRIME. It was. I glanced at the first page, entitled "HOW TO TELL A CROOK": "G-Men have found that crooks cannot look an honest man in the eye. Always look at the eyes of suspects for the telltale evidence." I remember the day I tried it on Grover Dill. "What are *you* lookin' at?" was all he said before he hit me in the mouth. I guess Melvin Purvis never had to deal with anybody like Grover Dill.

As you have no doubt deduced, there was a period in my life when I was an implacable foe of crime. Every week I listened intently as Warden Lawes of Sing Sing intoned on the radio: "Attention! All citizens be on the lookout for Harry Rottenstone, known as Harry the Fink, wanted for armed robbery in Oklahoma. He is five feet, eight and one half inches tall, usually of mean disposition, a diagonal scar running from left ear to jaw, steel-blue eyes, tattoo on right forearm of red heart: MOTHER. This man is armed and presumed dangerous. Notify the police. Do *not* attempt to take him singlehandedly.

285

Notify your local law-enforcement office. This is Warden Lawes saying 'Good night.'"

Every day after that, I coolly surveyed all passing strangers for telltale scars. Eventually it had to happen, and it did. I spotted a thickset steelworker getting on a bus and ten minutes later reported him to the big cop who helped kids across the street in front of Warren G. Harding School. The feeling of stark righteousness and bravery that I experienced at that moment, coupled with my natural fear of cops, is still fresh in my memory.

"Officer! I just saw Harry the Fink! He got on the Island Steel bus!"

"Harry who?"

"Harry the Fink! I heard about him on the radio. He robbed Oklahoma!"

"Oh, for God sake! You're the ninth kid today that's seen Harry the Fink! Last week it was Iron-Lip Louie. They oughta make listening to that damn Sing Sing program against the law. I'll Harry-the-Fink you! Get in school. You're late."

Between Warden Lawes and Mr. Keene, Tracer of Lost Persons, the cops must had had their hands full night and day. Mr. Keene was always announcing about how somebody had wandered away from his wife and seven kids in Minneapolis and was last seen wearing a blue suit and driving a black Plymouth with the name "Bubbles" written on the trunk. A population with its eye peeled for runaway husbands and escaped embezzlers did not make things easy down at the old precinct house.

I knew that somewhere under this pile of junk must be my FBI in Peace and War Official Fingerprint Kit, for which I had sent in two Lava soap wrappers. You *needed* Lava soap to get that crummy, sticky black ink off your fingers after you got the kit. I remember running the rubber roller, loaded with ink, right up the back of my kid brother's neck, a dismal incident that could well have been one of the contributing factors that led directly to World War Two.

A flash of red caught my eye and another trophy of another long-lost afternoon confronted me, a battered, bright-red plastic fireman's hat bearing the motto: ED WYNN TEXACO FIRE CHIEF. For one brief, feverish season, this Fire Chief hat was an absolute *must* for every right-thinking kid. Ed Wynn came on the radio with that big old siren, with the fire bells banging, wearing a hat exactly like this beauty. They gave them away at the Texaco station to anybody who could afford gas, and also at the World's Fair.

Gingerly, I placed it atop my head to see if it still gave me that old feeling of pizzazz. I arose, walked to the window and, for reasons that are obscure to me, raised the glass and stuck my head out, high over the roaring canyon of the Manhattan street. The sun bore down weakly as I said to myself:

"You are absolutely the only guy in all of New York that is wearing an Ed Wynn Fire Chief hat at this minute. You are unique. Hurray!"

At that instant, a gust of frigid wind struck me smartly on the left side of my cranium. I felt the Fire Chief hat lift slightly, and in an instant it was gone. I stared as it turned over and over, drifting down toward the traffic jam, a tiny, red, uproarious Ed Wynn horselaugh volplaning down to the sidewalk.

In a panic, I rushed into the kitchen and pressed the button on the phone that connected me with the doorman far below. His voice filtered up through the hum.

"Yeah?"

"MY FIRE CHIEF HAT JUST FELL OUT OF THE WINDOW!"

"Yer what?"

"My, uh–" I suddenly realized what I was saying. "My, uh–my Fire Chief hat."

"Fire Chief hat–out the window."

"It's red! It says Ed Wynn on it."

"Ed who?"

"WYNN! ED WYNN!" I was shouting.

"Don't he live on the third floor? In 3-C?"

"NO! ED WYNN, THE FIRE CHIEF!"

"You got a *fire?* You want me to call–"

"LOOK, GODDAMN IT! THERE'S A RED FIRE CHIEF HAT ON THE SIDEWALK IN FRONT OF THIS BUILDING, GET IT AND BRING IT UP TO ME!"

There was a long pause, until finally: "OK. If you say so. . . ." He hung up. I rushed back to the window to peer down. Sure enough, I could see the midget figure of the doorman far below, looking up and down the street. My God! A tiny kid had my hat on his head! Without thinking, I shouted down 16 floors:

288

"GIMME BACK MY HAT, KID!"

Instantly, dozens of passers-by peered up, hoping to see another suicide. I saw the doorman tangle with the struggling kid far below. A few shadowy faces appeared at apartment windows across the avenue. Stealthily, I pulled down the window and hid behind my madras drapes. What am I doing? Skulking back to the sofa— my Jack Armstrong Pedometer clicking, the cockamamie on my left hand glowing brightly—I sat down and tried to get a grip on myself. I know what I'll do. I'll wrap all this junk up, throw it in the back of the closet, get dressed and go down to P.J.'s. The hell with this. I'm a grown-up man. What do I want with an Ed Wynn Fire Chief hat?

It was no use. I couldn't kid myself. I wanted my hat back. For years I had never once thought of my hat and didn't even know I still had it, and now I wanted it more than anything in the world. Even my cutout cardboard Grumpy mask, which I got from *Pepper Young's Family*, didn't seem to help. I stuck my nose through the cutout hole in the mask and snapped the two cracked rubber bands over my ears, my eyes staring bleakly out through the slits in Grumpy's map.

I sat for a moment, wanting to go back to the window to see how the doorman was doing but afraid they'd spot me across the way. Suppressing the thought, I returned to the box and resumed my excavations. Rummaging about, I next rediscovered my old blue-steel bicycle clip for my pants. I snapped it on the left leg of my pajamas to see if my ankles had gotten fatter. It was then that I noticed my old canvas delivery bag from the time I had a magazine route: COLLIER'S, LIBERTY MAGAZINE WAS emblazoned in red letters on the side. Tucked in the bag was an old Nabisco Shredded Wheat Color Card. I could see where I had badly colored Niagara Falls with Crayolas. I pulled the shoulder strap down over my neck and was amazed to find that the bag came up under my armpit. It used to hang down around my knees. It must have shrunk. I was attempting to adjust it when my doorbell rang.

He's got it! I leaped to the door, flinging it open. Al, the Ukrainian doorman, stood in the hallway, holding my Ed Wynn Fire Chief hat.

"You got it! GREAT!"

"That kid sure put up a fight." He extended his paw, holding the battered plastic helmet.

"He can get his *own* hat!" I hissed. I noticed that Al had an odd look on his face.

"How come you're wearin' that mask, mister?"

I had forgotten completely about my false face, which I was still wearing. I figured I'd better play it cool:

"Oh. that's Grumpy. I'm doing a little work here this morning."

"Oh, I see," he said, backing off a bit as he noticed my bicycle clip and my *Collier's* delivery bag.

I reached out for the Fire Chief hat and knew immediately that I had made another mistake. The screaming yellow Jap on my hand, his blood gushing forth, lit up the entire hallway. Al started slightly and said:

"I never knew you was in the Marines. I was in the

Navy. You oughta see the tattoo I got on my backside!
Gung Ho!"

"Oh, that. I was just doing a little painting around
here."

As I took the precious Fire Chief hat from his grubby
claw, he noticed the Jack Armstrong Pedometer that
hung from my right knee.

Retreating hastily—clicking with each step—I mumbled
my thanks and slammed the door. There was no doubt
about it. I knew I would have to move. When the doorman told this story around, I would be cooked.

Pouring myself a neat brandy, I began to straighten
up the joint, ruffling through the still-untapped drift
of effluvia that remained in the box. What further horrors
lay here entombed? What as-yet-unrealized embarrass-
ments? There was my Joe Palooka Big Little Book, my
Junior Birdmen of America Senior Pilot's License, even
the four-color Magic Slide Rule Patented Piano Lesson
that had guaranteed to teach me to play in just seven
minutes. There was my Mystic Ventril-O, with which I
had unsuccessfully attempted to mystify my friends by
throwing my voice into trunks, hollering in a comb-and-
tissue-paper voice: "HELP! Let me out!" There was my
Charles Atlas Dynamic-Tension Muscle-Building and
Chest Expanding Course, my periscope, my match-cover
collection, the magnifying glass with which I had set
Helen Weathers on fire. It was all there.

Gingerly I tilted the huge box over onto its side. A
tinkling, squeaking, musty avalanche spilled out over the
floor—and my benighted youth lay shimmering before me

like some surrealistic collage of adolescent dreams: my Tom Mix Whistling Ring, which never whistled; my Captain Midnight Photomatic Code-O-Graph badge and Secret Squadron Bomber Wings, which lost their pin the very first instant I tried to attach them to my pullover and caused a fit of hysterics that has become legendary in my family, a fit that resulted in my mother banning *Captain Midnight* listening in our house for almost a month. Rolled in a sad little ball were the tattered remains of my Jack Armstrong pennant from Hudson High, a school that, by an odd coincidence, flew the same colors as the orange-and-white Wheaties box. I thought for a moment how well it would look over my desk at the office, and then sadly dismissed the thought. Lovingly, I fingered my Huskies Club pin, an athletic organization sponsored by the people who manufactured Grape-Nuts, a cereal that I remembered chiefly for its ability to crack false teeth. For a moment I stared off into the middle distance, seeing with stark clarity that dramatic instant when my grandmother's dentures shattered with a loud report on a mighty spoonful of that nutlike cereal, known for its gentle laxative action. Grandma was never quite the same after that. Lou Gehrig, who was the president of the Huskies Club, maintained in many a comic-strip advertisement that it was because of Grape-Nuts that he was able to follow Babe Ruth in the Yankee batting order.

A tiny, shriveled square of cloth next caught my eye. Great balls of fire! My Sky Blazers Arm Patch, which proved conclusively that I ate two slices of Wonder

Bread every day. Tom Mix Straight Shooter premiums, long forgotten but never forgiven, emerged; and a Tom Mix Special Sun Watch, to be used when lost in the jungles of Yucatán, a place I have always half suspected I would end up in, anyway. If you're lost in the head-hunter-ridden jungles, you'd better know what time it is. My pulse quickened as I extracted from the grisly array a device that could come in even handier: my Tom Mix Periscope Ring. I dusted it off and slipped it on my pinkie. Holding it up to my eye, I could see in hazy outline the bathroom door—*behind* me! The uses for such a device are obvious, especially around an office filled with ambitious, bushy-tailed young executives on the make.

Did mine eyes deceive me? No. Beneath a pair of Tom Mix spurs lurked my most occult treasure, a genuine Mystic Voodoo Skull Ring, with genuine simulated emerald eyes—a ring designed to put curses on your enemies. There is no doubt that such a ring could still have its uses. I slipped it carefully into my pocket, already formulating plans. Next came an *objet* of such poignant personal meaning that instinctively I turned my eyes away from it. Its very presence brought back an afternoon that even today rankles in my soul as one of those really terrible things that happen to all of us. My Uncle Ned had given me a dollar bill for my ninth birthday. Crisp, clean, of a beautiful green color, I held it for an all-too-brief time. Minutes later, I stood in front of a diabolical machine at the candy store, a machine filled with such tremendous bonanzas as Brownie cameras, wrist watches and cigarette lighters embossed with naked ladies; flash-lights made in the form of tiny revolvers, all floating in a sea of multicolored candy BBs. All you had to do to get one of these treasures was to skillfully operate two chromium handles, which in turn maneuvered the claw of a tiny steam shovel inside the case. Nickel after nickel I poured into this monster, growing more nervous and sweaty as each time the claw didn't *quite* grab the Brownie. Finally, after 85 cents had gone down the drain, it threw me a contemptible lead watch fob bearing the likeness of Myrna Loy.

I sucked moodily on my long-lost Dr. Christian Bubble Pipe. An angry wind laden with sooty ice crystals banged briefly at the windows of my apartment. It was getting colder. Sadly I returned it to the dusty magic mountain of illusion—lost and gone, grieved by only the wind. I had had enough. Back into the box I stuffed Brownie, Wimpy, Grumpy, Ed Wynn, Roscoe Turner, Jack Armstrong, Melvin Purvis, Buck Rogers—the whole teeming throng of them from out of the past. Over this communal crypt I laid the Dead Sea Scrolls—carefully smoothed newspaper fragments bearing the faded face of Harold Teen, and Perry Winkle's round sailor hat, and the yellowed headline "DAYLIGHT RAID ON NORMANDY PORTS. B-17S BOMB COAST."

Replacing the cover, I twisted the wires back together, binding the whole thing in place. For a fleeting moment, I considered shoving the whole sorry mess out onto the garbage landing. But I chickened out. Staggering under the load, I dragged my childhood to the hall closet. With an enormous effort, I got it up to the top shelf. Mysterious rattles and tinkles and squeakings continued for a few seconds. Then, silence—except for the muffled, jaunty quackings of my old rubber duck. I read the lettering on the box again: LIFE—THE COMPLETE CEREAL. I wondered whether my mother had picked that box purposely. You never know about mothers.

Outside, the long December afternoon was darkening into night. It wouldn't be long before the crowds of Christmas shoppers and Rockefeller Center holiday rubes would give way to the big-time, out-on-the-town crowd. Across the avenue, Christmas trees glowed through Venetian blinds. From the apartment next door drifted the nasal tones of a 12-year-old protest caroler singing *Jesus Don't Love Me Anymore, but I Got You, Babe,* the current spiritual smash, to the accompaniment of his electric tambourine.

I sat for a long moment in the gathering gloom and then suddenly noticed the huddled form of my little green aluminum Japanese Christmas tree. On impulse, I fished around in the rubble on my coffee table and came up with a thin, dime-sized copper disk with the faded inscription POPEYE SPINACH EATERS' LUCKY PIECE. Cradling it in my sweaty palm, I picked up the Christmas tree and gingerly unscrewed the fuse that I had twisted to death. With my forefinger, I carefully inserted my old badge of spinach addiction and Popeye fandom. Magically, the thin but unmistakable notes of "I'm dream-

295

ing of a white Christmas" filled the room and the tiny tree began to pirouette, its hidden mechanisms working flawlessly, its miniature red and green, blue and yellow candles sending out a dazzling rainbow of soft Christmas cheer. Lovingly, I place it on the window sill for the world to see. Popeye had saved the day again.

WANDA HICKEY'S NIGHT OF GOLDEN MEMORIES

Puberty rites in the more primitive tribal societies are almost invariably painful and traumatic experiences."

I half dozed in front of my TV set as the speaker droned on in his high, nasal voice. One night a week, as a form of masochistic self-discipline, I sentence myself to a minimum of three hours viewing educational television. Like so many other things in life, educational TV is a great idea but a miserable reality: murky films of home life in Kurdistan, jowly English authors being interviewed by jowly English literary critics, pinched-faced ladies demonstrating Japanese brush techniques. But I watch all of it religiously—I suppose because it is there, like Mount Everest.

"A classic example is the Ugga Buggah tribe of lower Micronesia," the speaker continued, tapping a pointer on the map behind him.

A shot of an Ugga Buggah teenager appeared on the

screen, eyes rolling in misery, face bathed in sweat. I leaned forward. His expression was strangely familiar.

"When an Ugga Buggah reaches puberty, the rites are rigorous and unvarying for both sexes. Difficult dances are performed and the candidate for adulthood must eat a sickening ritual meal during the postdance banquet. You will also notice that his costume is as uncomfortable as it is decorative."

Again the Ugga Buggah appeared, clothed in a garment that seemed to be made of feathers and chain mail, the top grasping his Adam's apple like an iron clamp, his tongue lolling out in pain.

"The adults attend these tribal rituals only as chaperones and observers, and look upon the ceremony with indulgence. Here we see the ritual dance in progress."

A heavy rumble of drums; then a moiling herd of sweating feather-clad dancers of both sexes appeared on screen amid a great cloud of dust.

"Of course, we in more sophisticated societies no longer observe these rites."

Somehow, the scene was too painful for me to continue watching. Something dark and lurking had been awakened in my breast.

"What the hell you mean we don't observe puberty rites?" I mumbled rhetorically as I got up and switched off the set. Reaching up to the top bookshelf, I took down a leatherette-covered volume. It was my high school class yearbook. I leafed through the pages of photographs: beaming biology teachers, pimply-faced students, lantern-jawed football coaches. Suddenly, there it was—a sharply etched photographic record of a true puberty rite among the primitive tribes of northern Indiana.

The caption read: "The Junior Prom was heartily enjoyed by one and all. The annual event was held this year at the Cherrywood Country Club. Mickey Eisley and his Magic Music Makers provided the romantic rhythms. All agreed that it was an unforgettable evening, the memory of which we will all cherish in the years to come."

True enough. In the gathering gloom of my Manhattan apartment, it all came back.

"You going to the prom?" asked Schwartz, as we chewed on our salami sandwiches under the stands of the football field, where we preferred for some reason to take lunch at that period of our lives.

"Yep, I guess so," I answered as coolly as I could.

"Who ya takin'?" Flick joined the discussion, sucking at a bottle of Nehi orange.

"I don't know. I was thinking of Daphne Bigelow." I had dropped the name of the most spectacular girl in the entire high school, if not the state of Indiana itself.

"No kidding!" Schwartz reacted in a tone of proper awe and respect, tinged with disbelief.

"Yeh. I figure I'd give her a break."

Flick snorted, the gassy orange pop going down the wrong pipe. He coughed and wheezed brokenly for several moments. I had once dated Daphne Bigelow and, although the occasion, as faithful readers will recall, was not a riotous success, I felt that I was still in the

301

running. Several occasions in the past month had led me to believe that I was making a comeback with Daphne. Twice she had distinctly acknowledged my presence in the halls between classes, once actually speaking to me.

"Oh, hi there, Fred," she had said in that musical voice.

"Uh . . . hi, Daph," I had replied wittily. The fact that my name is not Fred is neither here nor there; she had *spoken* to me. She had remembered my face from somewhere.

"Ya gotta go formal," said Schwartz. "I read on the bulletin board where it said you wear a summer formal to the prom."

"No kidding?" Flick had finished off the orange and was now fully with us. "What's a summer formal?"

"That's where you wear one of those white coats," I explained. I was known as the resident expert in our group on all forms of high life. This was because my mother was a fanatical Fred Astaire fan.

"Ya gotta rent 'em," I said with the finality of an expert.

Two weeks later, each one of us received a prim white envelope containing an engraved invitation.

> *The Junior Class is proud to invite you to the Junior Prom, to be held at the Cherrywood Country Club beginning eight P.M. June fifth. Dance to the music of Mickey Eisley and his Magic Music Makers.*
>
> *Summer formal required.*
>
> *The Committee*

It was the first engraved invitation I had ever received. The puberty rites had begun. That night around the supper table, the talk was of nothing else.

"Who ya gonna take?" my old man asked, getting right to the heart of the issue. Who you were taking to the prom was considered a highly significant decision, possibly affecting your whole life, which, in some tragic cases, it did.

"Oh, I don't know. I was thinking of a couple of girls." I replied in an offhand manner, as though this slight detail didn't concern me at all. My kid brother, who was taking all this in with sardonic interest, sneered derisively and went back to shoveling in his red cabbage. He had not yet discovered girls. My mother paused while slicing the meat loaf.

"Why not take that nice Wanda Hickey?"

"Aw, come on, Ma. This is the prom. This is important. You don't take Wanda Hickey to the *prom*."

Wanda Hickey was the only girl who I knew for an absolute fact liked me. Ever since we had been in third grade, Wanda had been hanging around the outskirts of my social circle. She laughed at my jokes and once, when we were 12, actually sent me a valentine. She was always loitering around the tennis courts, the ball diamonds, the alleys where on long summer nights we played Kick the Can or siphoned gas to keep Flick's Chevy running. In fact, there were times when I couldn't shake her.

"Nah, I haven't decided who I'm gonna take. I was kind of thinking of Daphne Bigelow."

The old man set his bottle of Pabst Blue Ribbon down

303

carefully on the table. Daphne Bigelow was the daughter of one of the larger men in town. There was, in truth, a street named after her family.

"You're a real glutton for punishment, ain't you?" The old man flicked a spot of foam off the table. He was referring to an unforgettable evening I had once spent with Daphne in my callow youth. "Oh, well, you might as well learn your lesson once and for all."

He was in one of his philosophical moods. The White Sox had dropped nine straight, and a losing streak like that usually brought out his fatalistic side. He leaned back in his chair, blew some smoke toward the ceiling and went on: "Yep. Too many guys settle for the first skirt that shows up. And regret it the rest of their lives."

Ignoring the innuendo, my mother set the mashed potatoes down on the table and said, "Well, I think Wanda is a very nice girl. But then, what I think doesn't matter."

My mother had the practiced turn of phrase of the veteran martyr, whose role in life is to suffer as publicly as possible.

"I gotta rent a summer formal," I announced.

"Christ, you gonna wear one a' them monkey suits?" the old man chuckled. He had never, to my knowledge, worn anything more formal than a sports jacket in his entire life.

"I'm going down to that place on Hohman Avenue tomorrow with Schwartz and see about it."

"Oh, boy! Lah-di-dah," said my kid brother with

characteristically eloquent understatement. Like father, like son.

The next day, after school, Schwartz and I went downtown to a place we both had passed countless times in our daily meanderings. Hanging out over the street was the cutout of a tall, creamfaced man dressed to the nines in high silk hat, stiff starched shirt, swallow-tailed coat, striped morning trousers and an ivory-headed walking stick held with an easy grace by his dove-gray gloved hand. To read, spluttering neon script underneath: AL'S SWANK FORMALWEAR. RENTED BY THE DAY OR HOUR. FREE FITTINGS.

We climbed the narrow, dark wooden steps to the second floor. Within a red arrow painted on the wall were the words SWANK FORMAL—TURN LEFT.

We went past a couple of dentists' offices and a door marked BAIL BONDSMAN—FREEDOM FOR *you* DAY OR NIGHT.

"I wonder if Fred Astaire ever comes here," Schwartz said.

"Oh, come on, Schwartz. This is serious!" I could feel excitement rising deep inside me. The prom, the engraved invitation, the summer formal; it was all starting to come together.

Al's Swank Formalwear turned out to be a small room with a yellow light bulb hanging from the ceiling, a couple of tall glass cases containing suits on hangers, a counter and a couple of smudgy full-length mirrors. Schwartz opened negotiations with a swarthy, bald, hawk-eyed, shirt-sleeved man behind the counter. Around his neck hung a yellow measuring tape. He wore a worn vest with a half-dozen chalk pencils sticking out of the pocket.

"Uh . . . we'd like to . . . uh . . ." Schwartz began confidently

"OK, boys. Ya wanna make it big at the prom, am I right? Ya come to the right place. Ya goin' to that hop out at Cherrywood, right?"

"Uh . . . yeah," I replied.

"And ya wanna summah fawmal, right?"

"HEY, MORTY!" he shouted out. "HERE'S TWO MORE FOR THAT BASH AT CHERRYWOOD. I'D SAY ONE THIRTY-SIX SHAWT, ONE FAWTY REGU-LAH." His practiced eye had immediately sized us correctly.

"COMIN' UP!" Morty's voice echoed from the bowels of the establishment.

Humming to himself, Al began to pile and unpile boxes like we weren't even there. I looked around the room at the posters of various smartly turned out men of the world. One in particular, wearing a summer formal, had a striking resemblance to Cesar Romero, his distinguished gray sideburns and bronze face contrasting nicely with the snowy whiteness of his jacket.

There was another picture, of Tony Martin, who was at that time at the peak of his movie career, usually portraying Arab princes who disguised themselves as beggars in order to make the scene at the market place. He was always falling in love with a slave girl who turned out to be a princess in disguise, played by Paulette Goddard. Tony's roguish grin, somewhat flyspecked, showed that he was about to break into *Desert Song*.

Schwartz was busily inspecting a collection of bow ties displayed under glass in one of the showcases.

"OK ON THE THIRTY-SIX SHAWT, AL, BUT I'M OUTA FAWTIES. HOW 'BOUT THAT FAWTY-TWO REGULAH THAT JUST CAME BACK FROM THAT DAGO WEDDING?" shouted Morty from the back room.

"CUT THE TALK AN' BRING THE GOODS!" Al shouted back, straightening up, his face flushed.

"THE FAWTY-TWO AIN'T BEEN CLEANED YET!" came from the back room.

"BRING IT OUT, AWREADY!" barked Al. He turned to me.

"This suit just come in from anotha job. Don't worry about how it looks. We'll clean it up an' take it in so's it'll fit good."

Morty emerged, a tall, thin, sad man in a gray smock, even balder than Al. He carried two suits on hangers, draped them over the counter, gave Al a dirty look and stalked back into the shadows.

"OK now, boys. First you." Al nodded to Schwartz. "Take this and try it on behind the curtain. It should fit good. It's maybe a little long at the cuffs, but we'll take them up."

Schwartz grabbed the hanger and scurried behind the green curtain. Al held up the other suit. In the middle of a dark reddish-brown stain that covered the entire right breast pocket was a neat little hole right through the jacket. Al turned the hanger around and stuck his finger through the hole.

"HEY, MORTY!" he shouted.

"WHAT NOW?"

"HOW 'BOUT THIS HOLE INNA FAWTY-TWO? CAN YA FIX IT BY TONIGHT?"

"WADDAYA WANT, MIRACLES?" Morty whined.

"Don't worry, kid. We can fix this up good as new. You'll never tell it ain't a new coat."

Schwartz emerged from the fitting room shrouded in what looked like a parachute with sleeves.

"Perfect! Couldn't be bettuh!" shouted Al exultantly, darting from behind the counter. He grabbed Schwartz by the shoulders, spun him around and, with a single movement, ran his hand up into Schwartz' crotch, measured the inseam, spun him around again, made two pencil marks on the sleeves—which came almost to his finger tips—yanked up the collar, punched him smartly in the kidney, all the while murmuring in a hoarse stage whisper:

"It's made for you. Just perfect. Couldn't be bettuh. Perfect. Like tailormade."

Schwartz smiled weakly throughout the ordeal.

"OK, kid, take it off. I'll have it ready for you next week."

Obediently, Schwartz disappeared into the fitting room. Al turned to me. "Here, slip on this coat." He held it out invitingly. I plunged my arms into its voluminous folds. I felt his iron grip on my shoulder blades as he yanked me upward and spun me around, his appraising eye darting everywhere.

"Just perfect. Couldn't be bettuh. Fits like a glove. Take it in a little here; pull in the bias here. . . ."

He took out his chalk and made a few marks on my back.

"OK. Slip outa it."

Al again thrust his finger through the hole.

"Reweave it like new. An' doan worry 'bout the stain; we'll get it out. Musta boon oomo party. Horo, try on these pants."

He tossed a pair of midnight-blue trousers over the counter at me. Inside the hot little cubicle, as I changed into the pants, I stroked the broad black-velvet stripe that lined the outer seam. I was really in the big time now. They were rumpled, of course, and they smelled strongly of some spilled beverage, but they were truly magnificent. The waist came to just a shade below my armpits, beautifully pleated. Tossing the curtain aside, I sashayed out like Cary Grant.

"Stand up straight, kid," Al breathed into my ear. An aromatic blast of pastrami and pickled herring made my head reel.

"Ah. Perfect. Just right. Put a little tuck in the waist, so." He grabbed several yards of the seat. "And a little in here." A sudden thrill of pain as he violently measured the inseam. Then it was all over.

"Now," he said, back behind his counter once again, "how do ya see the shirts? You want 'em straight or ruffled? Or pleated, maybe? Very smart." He indicated several shirts on display in his grimy glass case. "I would recommend our Monte Carlo model, a real spiffy numbah."

We both peered down at the shirts. The Monte Carlo number was, indeed, spiffy, its wide, stiff, V-cut collar arching over cascading ribbons of razor-sharp pleats.

"Boy, now that's a shirt!" Schwartz breathed excitedly.

"That what *I* want," I said aloud. No other shirt would do.

"Me, too," Schwartz seconded.

"OK now," Al continued briskly, "how 'bout studs? Ya got 'em?"

"Uh. . . . what?"

He had caught me off guard. I had heard the word "stud" before, but never in a tailor shop.

"OK, I guess not. I'll throw 'em in. Because you're high-class customers. Now, I suppose ya wanna go first-class, right?"

Al directed this question at both of us, his face assuming a look of concerned forthrightness.

"Right?" he repeated.

"Yeah." Schwartz answered uncertainly for both of us.

"I knew that the minute you two walked in. Now, I'm gonna show you somepin that is exclusive with Al's Swank Formalwear."

With an air of surreptitious mystery, he bent over, slid open a drawer and placed atop the counter an object that unfocused my eyes with its sheer kaleidoscopic brilliance.

"No place else in town can supply you with a genuwine Hollywood paisley cummabund. It's our trademark."

I stared at the magnificent band of glowing, scintillating fabric, already seeing myself a total smash on the dance floor.

"It's only a buck extra. And worth five times the price. Adolphe Menjou always wears this model. How 'bout it, men?"

We both agreed in unison. After all, you only live once.

"Of course, included for only half a dolla more is our luwmal bow tie and matchin' booteneer. I would suggest the maroon."

"Sounds great," I answered.

"Isn't that everything?" asked Schwartz with some concern.

"Is that all! You gotta be kiddin', sonny. How do you expect to trip the light fantastic without a pair a black patent-leatha dancin' pumps?"

"Dancin' what?" I asked.

"Shoes, shoes," he explained irritably. "And we throw in the socks for nuttin'. How 'bout it?"

"Well, uh. . . ."

"Fine! So that's it, boys. I'll have everything all ready the day before the Prom. You'll really knock 'em dead."

As we left, another loud argument broke out between Morty and Al. Their voices accompanied us down the long flight of narrow stairs and out into the street.

Step by step, in the ancient tradition, the tribal ritual was being acted out. The prom, which was now two weeks off, began to occupy our minds most of the waking day. The semester had just about played itself out; our junior year was almost over. The trees and flowers were in blossom, great white clouds drifted across deep-blue skies and baseball practice was in full swing—but somehow, this spring was different from the rest. The prom was something that we had heard about since our earliest days. A kind of golden aura hung over the word itself. Every couple of days, the P.A. at school announced that the prom committee was meeting or requesting something.

There was only one thing wrong. As each day ticked inexorably by toward that magic night at the Cherrywood Country Club, I still could not steel myself to actually seek out Daphne Bigelow and ask her the fatal question. Time and again, I spotted her in the halls, drifting by on gossamer wings, her radiant complexion casting a glow on all those around her, her brilliant smile lighting up the corners of 202 homeroom. But each time, I broke into a fevered sweat and chickened out at the last instant.

The weekend before the prom was sheer torture. Schwartz, always efficient and methodical, had already made all his plans. We sat on the back steps of my porch late Sunday afternoon, watching Lud Kissel next door struggle vainly to adjust the idling speed on his time-ravaged carburetor so that the family Nash didn't stall at 35 miles an hour. He had been drinking, of course, so it was quite a show.

"How ya doin' with Daphne Bigelow?" asked Schwartz sardonically, knowing full well the answer.

"Oh, that. I haven't had time to ask her," I lied.

"Ya better get on the stick. There's only a week left."

"Who *you* got lined up?" I asked, tossing a pebble at old Lud, who was now asleep under his running board.

"Clara Mae Mattingly," Schwartz replied in a steady, expressionless voice.

I was surprised. Clara Mae was one of those shadowy, quiet girls who rarely were mentioned outside of honor rolls and stuff like that. She wore gold-rimmed glasses and still had pigtails.

"Yep," Schwartz added smugly, gratified by my re-uotlon.

"Boy, she sure can spell." It was all I could think of to say that was good about her, other than the fact that she was female.

"Sure can," Schwartz agreed. He, too, had been quite a speller in our grade school days; and on more than one occasion, Clara Mae had demolished him with a brilliant display of virtuosity in a school-wide spelldown, a form of verbal Indian wrestling now almost extinct but which at one time was a Waterloo for many of us among the unlettered. Clara Mae had actually once gone to the state final and had lost out to a gangly farm girl from downstate who apparently had nothing else to do down there but read *Webster*'s through the long winter nights.

"You gonna send her a corsage?" I asked.

"Already ordered it. At the Cupid Florist." Schwartz' self-satisfaction was overflowing.

"An orchid?"

"Yep. Cost eight bucks."

"Holy God! Eight bucks!" I was truly impressed.

"That includes a gold pin for it."

Our conversation trailed off as Lud Kissel rose heavily to his knees and crawled off down the driveway on all fours, heading for the Bluebird Tavern, which was closed on Sundays. Lud always got restless in the spring.

A few hours later, after supper, I went out gloomily to water the lawn, a job that purportedly went toward earning my allowance, which had reached an all-time high that spring of three dollars a week. Fireflies played about the cottonwoods in the hazy twilight, but I was troubled. One week to go; less, now, because you couldn't count the day of the prom itself. In the drawer where I kept my socks and scout knife, buried deep in the back, were 24 one-dollar bills, which I had saved for the prom. Just as deep in my cowardly soul, I knew I could never ask Daphne Bigelow to be my date.

Refusing to admit it to myself, I whistled moodily as I sprayed the irises and watched a couple of low-flying bats as they skimmed over the lawn and up into the poplars. Mrs. Kissel, next door, creaked back and forth on her porch swing, a copy of *True Romances* open in her lap, as she waited for Lud's return with his usual snootful. My kid brother came out onto the porch and, from sheer habit, I quickly shot a stream of water over him, catching him in mid-air as he leaped high to avoid the stream. It was a superbly executed shot. I had led him just right. He caught it full in the chest, his yellow polo shirt clinging to his ribs wetly, like a second skin. Bawling at the top of his lungs, he disappeared into the house and slammed the screen door

314

behind him. Ordinarily, this small triumph would have cheered me up for hours; but tonight, I tasted nothing but ashes. Suddenly, his face reappeared in the doorway.

"I'M GONNA TELL MA!" he yelled.

Instantly, like a cobra, I struck. Sweeping the stream quickly over the screen door, I got him again. Another scream of rage and he was gone. Again, I sank into my moody sea of reflection. Was I going to boot the prom?

Flick had asked Janie Hutchinson, a tall, funny girl who had been in our class since kindergarten. And Schwartz was lined up with Clara Mae; all he had talked about that week had been that crummy orchid and how good a dancer he was. Flick had stopped asking me about Daphne ever since the past Wednesday, when I had gotten mad because he'd been needling me. All week, I had been cleaning up my Ford for the big night. If there was one thing in my life that went all the way, my only true and total love, it was my Ford V8, a convertible that I had personally rebuilt at least 35 times. I knew every valve spring personally, had honed each valve, burnished every nut and bolt she carried. Tuesday, I had simonized her completely; Wednesday, I had repeated the job; and Thursday, I had polished the chrome until my knuckles ached and my back was stiff. I had spent the past two days minutely cleaning the interior, using a full can of saddle-soap on the worn leather. Everything was set to go, except for one thing—no girl.

A feeling of helpless rage settled over me as I continued spraying the lawn. I flushed out a poor, hapless caterpillar from under a bush, squirting him mercilessly

315

full blast, until he washed down the sidewalk and disappeared into the weeds. I felt a twinge of evil satisfaction as he rolled over and over helplessly. It was getting dark. All that was left of the sun was a long purple-orange streak along the western horizon. The glow of the steel mills to the north and east began to light up the twilight sky. I had worked my way down to the edge of our weedy, pock-marked bed of sod when, out of the corner of my eye, I noticed something white approaching out of the gloom. I sprinkled on, not knowing that another piece was being fitted into the intricate mosaic of adolescence. I kicked absent-mindedly at a passing toad as I soaked down the dandelions.

"What are you doing?"

So deeply was I involved in self-pity that at first my mind wouldn't focus. Startled, I swung my hose around, spraying the white figure on the sidewalk ten feet away.

"I'm sorry!" I blurted out, seeing at once that I had washed down a girl dressed in white tennis clothes.

"Oh, hi, Wanda. I didn't see you there."

She dried herself with a Kleenex.

"What are you doing?" she asked again.

"I'm sprinkling the lawn." The toad hopped past, going the other way now. I squirted him briefly, out of general principles.

"You been playing tennis?" Since she was wearing tennis clothes and was carrying a racket, it seemed the right thing to say.

"Me and Eileen Akers were playing. Down at the park," she answered.

Eileen Akers was a sharp-faced, bespectacled girl I had, inexplicably, been briefly in love with in the third grade. I had come to my senses by the time we got into 4-B. It was a narrow escape. By then, I had begun to dimly perceive that there was more to women than being able to play a good game of Run Sheep, Run.

"I'm sure glad school's almost over," she went on, when I couldn't think of anything to say. "I can hardly wait. I never thought I'd be a senior."

"Yeah," I said.

"I'm going to camp this summer. Are you?"

"Yeah," I lied. I had a job already lined up for the summer, working for a surveyor. The next camp I would see would be in the Ozarks, and I'd be carrying an M-1.

Wanda swung her tennis racket at a June bug that flapped by barely above stall speed. She missed. The bug soared angrily up and whirred off into the darkness.

"Are you going to college when you graduate next year?" she asked. For some reason, I didn't like the drift of the conversation.

"Yeah, I guess so, if I don't get drafted."

"My brother's in the Army. He's in the Artillery." Her brother, Bud Hickey, was a tall, laconic type four or five years older than both of us.

"Yeah, I heard. Does he like it?"

"Well, he doesn't write much," she said. "But he's gonna get a pass next September, before he goes overseas."

"How come he's in the Artillery?" I asked.

317

"I don't know. They just put him there. I guess because he's tall."

"What's that gotta do with it? Do they have to *throw* the shells, or something?"

"I don't know. They just did it."

Then it happened. Without thinking, without even a shadow of a suspicion of planning, I heard myself asking: "You going to the prom?"

For a long instant she said nothing, just swung her tennis racket at the air.

"I guess so," she finally answered, weakly.

"It's gonna be great," I said, trying to change the subject.

"Uh . . . who are you going with?" She said it as if she really didn't care one way or the other.

"Well, I haven't exactly made up my mind yet." I bent down unconcernedly and pulled a giant milkweed out by the roots.

"Neither have I," she said.

It was then that I realized there was no sense fighting it. Some guys are born to dance forever with the Daphne Bigelows on shining ballroom floors under endless starry skies. Others—well, they do the best they can. I didn't know that yet, but I was beginning to suspect something.

"Wanda?"

"Yes?"

"Wanda. Would you . . . well . . . I mean . . . would you, you see, I was thinking. . . ."

"Yes?"

Here I go, in over the horns: "Wanda, uh . . . how about . . . going to the prom with me?"

She stopped twitching her tennis racket. The crickets cheeped, the spring air was filled with the sound of singing froglets. A soft breeze carried with it the promise of a rich summer and the vibrant aromas of a nearby refinery.

She began softly, "Of course, I've had a lot of invitations, but I didn't say yes to any of them yet. I guess it would be fun to go with you," she ended gamely.

"Yeah, well, naturally, I've had four or five girls who wanted to go with me, but I figured that they were mostly jerks anyway, and . . . ah . . . I meant to ask you all along."

The die was cast. There was no turning back. It was an ironclad rule. Once a girl was asked to the prom, only a total crumb would even consider ducking out of it. There had been one or two cases in the past, but the perpetrators had become socials pariahs, driven from the tribe to fend for themselves in the unfriendly woods.

Later that night, hunched over the kitchen table, still somewhat numbed by the unexpected turn of events, I chewed thoughtfully on a peanut-butter-and-jelly sandwich, while my mother, hanging over the sink in her rump-sprung Chinese-red chenille bathrobe, droned on monotonously: "You're just going to *have* to stop squirting Randy."

"Yeah," I answered, my mind three light-years away.

"You got his new Flash Gordon T-shirt all wet."

319

"Sorry," I said automatically. It was a phrase I used often in those days.

"It shrunk. And now he can't wear it."

"Why not?" I asked.

"It comes up around his chest now."

"Well, why can't he stretch it?"

"You just stop squirting him, that's all. You hear me?"

"It's a silly T-shirt, anyway," I said truculently.

"You heard what I said. No more squirting." That ended the conversation.

Later, in bed, I thought briefly of Daphne Bigelow, but was interrupted by a voice from the bed on the other side of the room.

"You rotten crumb. You squirted my T-shirt!"

"Ah, shaddup."

"You wait. I'm gonna get you!"

I laughed raucously. My kid brother wailed in rage.

"SHUT UP, YOU TWO! CUT OUT THE FIGHTING OR I'LL COME IN THERE AND DO SOME HEAD KNOCKING!"

The old man meant what he said and we knew it. I promptly fell asleep. It had been a long and tumultuous day.

I broke the news to Schwartz the next morning, after biology. We were hurrying through the halls between classes on our way to our lockers, which were side by side on the second floor.

"Hey, Schwartz, how about double-dating for the prom?" I asked. I knew he had no car and I needed moral support, anyway.

"Great! I'll help you clean up the car."

"I've already simonized her. She's all set."

"Are you gonna send Daphne an orchid, or what?"

"Well, no . . ." I said lamely, hoping he'd forget what he asked.

"What do you mean? Ya gotta send a corsage."

"Well, I *am* going to send a corsage."

"I thought you said you weren't."

I just couldn't shake him off. "I never said I wasn't gonna send a corsage."

"Are you nuts? You just said you weren't gonna."

"I'm not gonna send a corsage to Daphne Bigelow. You asked me if I was gonna send a corsage to Daphne. I'm not."

"She's gonna think you're a real cheap skate."

It was getting ridiculous. Schwartz was being even more of a numskull than usual.

"Schwartz, I have decided not to ask Daphne Bigelow to the prom."

He looked directly at me, which caused him to slam into two strolling freshman girls. Their books slid across the floor, where they were trampled underfoot by the thundering mob.

"Well, who *are* you taking?" he asked, oblivious to their shrieks of dismay.

"Wanda Hickey."

"*Wanda Hickey!*"

Schwartz was completely thrown by the bit of news. Wanda Hickey had never been what you could call a major star in our Milky Way. We walked on, saying

321

nothing, until finally, as we opened our lockers, Schwartz said: "Well, she sure is good at algebra."

It was true. Wanda was an algebra shark in the same way that Clara Mae was a spelling nut. Maybe we both got what we deserved.

Later that day, in the study hall, after I had polished off a history theme on some stupid thing like the Punic Wars, I got to thinking about Wanda. I could see her sitting way over on the other side of the room, a dusty sunbeam filtering through the window and lighting up her straw-colored hair. She was kind of cute. I'd never really noticed it before. Ever since second grade, Wanda had just been there, along with Eileen Akers, Helen Weathers and all the other girls who—along with me and Schwartz and Flick and Jossway and the rest—had moved together step by step up the creaky ladder of education. And here I was, at long last, taking Wanda Hickey—*Wanda Hickey*—to the prom, the only junior prom I would ever attend in my life.

As I chewed on the end of my fake-marble Wearever pen, I watched Wanda through half-closed eyes in the dusty sunbeam as she read *The Lady of the Lake*. Ahead of me, Schwartz dozed fitfully, as he always did in study hall, his forehead occasionally thumping the desk. Flick, to my right, struggled sullenly over his chemistry workbook. We both knew it was hopeless. Flick was the only one in our crowd who consistently flunked everything.

The prom was just five days away. This was the last week of school. Ahead our long summer in the sun stretched out like a lazy yellow road. For many of us, it was the last peaceful summer we were to know.

Mr. Wilson, the study-hall teacher, wandered aimlessly up and down the aisles, pretending he was interested in what we were pretending to be doing. From somewhere outside drifted the cries of a girls' volleyball game, while I drew pictures of my Ford on the inside cover of my three-ring notebook: front view, side view, rear view, outlining the drawings with ink.

That morning, on my way to school, I had gone down to the Cupid Florist Shop and ordered an orchid. My 24 dollars were shrinking fast. The eight-dollar bite for the orchid didn't help. Schwartz and I were going to split on the gas, which would come to maybe a buck apiece. After paying for the summer formal I'd have a fast ten dollars left for the night. As I sat in study hall, I calculated, writing the figures down, adding and substracting. But it didn't come out to much, no matter how I figured it.

Schwartz passed a note back to me. I opened it: "How about the Red Rooster afterward?"

I wrote underneath, "Where else?" and passed it back. The Red Rooster was part of the tribal ritual. It was *the* place you went after a big date, if you could afford it.

I glanced over across the room at Wanda and caught her looking at me. She instantly buried her head in her book. Good old Wanda.

On the way home from school every day that week of course, all we talked about was the prom. Flick was double-dating with Jossway and we were all going to meet afterward at the Rooster and roister until dawn, drinking deeply of the sweet elixir of the good life. The only thing that nagged me now was financial. Ten bucks didn't look as big as it usually did. Ordinarily, ten bucks could have gotten me through a month of just fooling around, but the prom was the big time.

Friday night, as I sat in the kitchen before going to bed, knocking down a liverwurst on whole wheat and drinking a glass of chocolate milk, the back door slammed open and in breezed the old man, carrying his bowling bag. Friday night was his big night down at the Pin-Bowl. He was a fanatical bowler, and a good one, too. He slid the bag across the floor, pretending to lay one down the groove, his right arm held out in a graceful follow-through, right leg trailing in the classic bowling stance.

"Right in the pocket," he said with satisfaction.

"How'd you do tonight?" I asked.

"Not bad. Had a two-oh-seven game. Damn near cracked six hundred."

He opened the refrigerator and fished around for a beer, then sat down heavily, took a deep drag from the bottle, burped loudly and said:

"Well, tomorrow's the big day, ain't it?"

"Yep," I answered. "Sure is."

"You takin' Daphne Bigelow?" he asked.

"Nah. Wanda Hickey."

"Oh, yeah? Well, you can't win 'em all. Wanda's old man is some kind of a foreman at the mill or something, ain't he?"

324

"I guess so."

"He drives a Studebaker Champion, don't he? The green two-door with the whitewalls."

The old man had a fine eye for cars. He judged all men by what they drove. Apparently a guy who drove a two-door Studebaker was not absolutely beyond the pale.

"Not a bad car. Except they burn oil after a while," he mused, omitting no aspects of the Studebaker.

"They used to have a weak front end. Bad kingpins." He shook his head critically, opening another beer and reaching for the rye bread.

I said nothing, lost in my own thoughts. My mother and kid brother had been in bed for an hour or so. We were, for all practical purposes, alone in the house. Next door, Mrs. Kissel threw out a pail of dishwater into the back yard with a swoosh. Her screen door slammed.

"How ya fixed for tomorrow night?" the old man asked suddenly, swirling his beer bottle around to raise the head.

"What do you mean?"

"I mean, how are ya *fixed?*"

My father never talked money to me. I got my allowance every Monday and that was that.

"Well, I've got about ten bucks."

"Hm." That was all he said.

After sitting in silence for a minute or so, he said, "You know, I always wished I coulda gone to a prom."

How can you answer something like that? He had

barely gotten out of eighth grade when he had to go
to work, and he never stopped for the rest of his life.

"Oh, well, what the hell." He finally answered himself.

He cut himself a slice of boiled ham and made a
sandwich.

"I was really hot tonight. Got a string of six straight
strikes in the second game. The old hook was movin',
getting a lot of wood."

He reached into his hip pocket, took out his wallet
and said:

"Look, don't tell Ma." He handed me a $20 bill.

"I had a couple of bets going on the second game,
and I'm a money bowler."

He was that. No doubt of it. In his early teens, he
had scrounged out a living as a pool shark, and he had
never lost the touch. I took the $20, glommed onto it
the way the proverbial drowning man grabs at a straw.
I was so astounded at this unprecedented gesture that
it never occurred to me to say thanks. He would have
been embarrassed if I had. A miracle had come to pass.
There was no doubt about it—the prom was going to be
an unqualified gas.

The next day dawned bright and sunny, as perfect
as a June day can be—in a steel-mill town. Even the
blast-furnace dust that drifted aimlessly through the soft
air glowed with promise. I was out early, dusting off the
car. It was going to be a top-down night. If there is
anything more romantic than a convertible with the top
down in June going to a prom, I'd like to hear about it.

Cleopatra's barge couldn't have been much more seductive.

My kid brother, his diminutive Flash Gordon T-shirt showing a great expanse of knobby backbone and skinny belly, yapped around me as I toiled over the Ford.

"Look what you done to my T-shirt!" he whined, his runny nose atrickle. He was in the midst of his annual spring cold, which would be superseded by his summer cold, which lasted nicely to the whopper he got in the fall, which, of course, was only a prelude to his winter-long *monster* cold.

"Stay away from the fender. You're dripping on it!" I shouted angrily, shoving him away.

"Flash Gordon's only about an inch high now!"

I couldn't help laughing. It was true. Flash had shrunk, along with the shirt, which Randy had earned by doggedly eating three boxes of Wheaties, saving the boxtops and mailing them in with 25 cents that he had, by dint of ferocious self-denial, saved from his 30-cent weekly allowance.

"Look, I'll get you another Flash Gordon T-shirt."

"You can't. They're not givin' 'em away no more. They're givin' away Donald Duck beanies with a propeller on top now."

"Well, then, stretch the one you got now, stupid."

"It won't stretch. It keeps getting littler."

He bounced up and down on a clothes pole, joggling the clothesline and my mother's wash. Within three seconds, she was out on the back porch.

"CUT IT OUT WITH THE CLOTHES POLE."

327

Sullenly, he slid off onto the ground. I went back to work, until the Ford gleamed like some rare jewel. Then I went into the house to begin the even more laborious process of getting *myself* in shape for the evening ahead. Locking the bathroom door, I took two showers, wearing a brand-new bar of Lifebuoy down to a nub. I knew what happened to people who didn't use it; every week, little comic strips underneath *Moon Mullins* told endless tales of disastrous proms due to dreaded B.O. It would not happen to me.

I then shaved for the second time that week, using a new Gillette Blue Blade. As usual when an important shave was executed, I nicked myself nastily in several places.

"Son of a bitch," I muttered, plastering the wounds with little pieces of toilet paper.

Carefully, I went over every inch of my face, battling that age-old enemy, the blackhead, and polished off the job with a copious application of stinging Aqua Velva. Next I attacked my hair, combing and recombing, getting just the right insouciant pitch to my pride and joy, my d.a. cut. Tonight, I would be a truly magnificent specimen of lusty manhood.

Twilight was fast approaching when I emerged from the bathroom, redolent of rare aromas, pink and svelte. But the real battle had not yet begun. Laid out on my bed was my beautiful summer formal. Al was right: The elegant white coat truly gleamed in virginal splendor. Not a trace of the red stain nor the sinister hole could be detected. The coat was ready for another night of celebration, its lapels spotless, its sleeves smooth and un-creased.

Carefully, I undid the pins that festooned my pleated Monte Carlo shirt. It was the damnedest thing I had ever seen, once I got it straightened out: long, trailing gauze-like shirttails, a crinkly front that thrummed like sheet metal and a collar that seemed to be carved of white rock. I slipped it on. Panic! It had no buttons—just holes.

Rummaging around frantically in the box the suit came in, I found a cellophane envelope containing little round black things. Ripping the envelope open, I poured them out; there were five of them, two of which immediately darted under the bed. From the looks of the remaining three, they certainly weren't buttons; but they'd have to do. Although I didn't know it at the time, I had observed a classic maneuver executed by at least one stud out of every set rented with a tux. Down on my hands and knees, already beginning to lose my Lifebuoy sheen, sweat popping out here and there, I scrambled around for the missing culprits.

The ordeal was well under way. Seven o'clock was approaching with such rapidity as to be almost unbe-lievable. Schwartz, Clara Mae and Wanda would *al-ready* be waiting for me, and here I was in my drawers, crawling around on my hands and knees. Finally, amid the dust and dead spiders under my bed, I found the two studs cowering together behind a hardball I'd lost three months earlier.

Back before the mirror again, I struggled to get them in place between the concrete slits. Sweat was beginning

329

to show under my arms. I got two in over my breastbone and now I tried to get the one at the collar over my Adam's apple. It was impossible! I could feel from deep within me several sobs beginning to form. The more I struggled, the more hamfisted I became. Oh, no! Two blackish thumb smudges appeared on my snowwhite collar.

"MA!" I screamed, "LOOK AT MY SHIRT!"

She rushed in from the kitchen, carrying a paring knife and a pan of apples. "What's the matter?"

"Look!" I pointed at the telltale prints.

My kid brother cackled in delight when he saw the trouble I was in.

"Don't touch it," she barked, taking control immediately. Dirty collars were her métier. She had fought them all her life. She darted out of the room and returned instantly with an artgum eraser.

"Now, hold still."

I obeyed as she carefully worked the stud in place and then artistically erased the two monstrous thumbprints. Never in my life had I experienced a collar remotely like the one that now clamped its iron grasp around my windpipe. Hard and unyielding, it dug mercilessly into my throat—a mere sample of what was to come.

"Where's your tie?" she asked. I had forgotten about that detail.

"It . . . ack . . . must be . . . in the box," I managed to gasp out. The collar had almost paralyzed my voice box.

She rummaged around and came up with the bow tie.

330

It was black and it had two metal clips. She snapped it onto the wing collar and stood back.

"Now, look at yourself in the mirror." I didn't recognize myself.

She picked up the midnight-blue trousers and held them open, so that I could slip into them without bending over.

True to his word, Al had, indeed, taken in the seat. The pants clamped me in a viselike grip that was to damn near emasculate me before the evening was out. I sucked in my stomach, buttoned the waistband tight, zippered up the fly and stood straight as a ramrod before the mirror. I had no other choice.

"Gimme your foot."

My mother was down on all fours, pulling the silky black socks onto my feet. Then, out of a box on the bed, she removed the gleaming pair of patent-leather dancing pumps, grabbed my right foot and shoved it into one of them, using her finger as a shoehorn. I tromped down. She squealed in pain.

"I can't get my finger out!"

I hobbled around, taking her finger with me.

"STAND STILL!" she screamed.

I stood like a crane, one foot in the air, with her finger jammed deep into the heel.

"RANDY! COME HERE!" she yelled.

My kid brother, who was sulking under the day bed, ran into the room.

"PULL HIS SHOE OFF, RANDY!" She was frantic.

"What for?" he asked sullenly.

"DON'T ASK STUPID QUESTIONS. JUST DO WHAT I SAY!"

I was getting an enormous cramp in my right buttock. "STAND STILL!" she yelled. "YOU'RE BREAKING MY FINGER!" Randy looked on impassively, observing a scene that he was later to weave into a family legend, embroidering it more and more as the years went by—making himself the hero, of course.

"RANDY! *Take off his shoe!*" Her voice quavered with pain and exasperation.

"He squirted my T-shirt."

"If you don't take off his shoe this instant, you're gonna regret it." This time, her voice was low and menacing. We both knew the tone. It was the end of the line.

Randy bent over and tugged off the shoe. My mother toppled backward in relief, rubbing her index finger, which was already blue.

"Go back under the day bed," she snapped. He scurried out of the room. I straightened out my leg—the cramp subsiding like a volcano in the marrow of my bones—and the gleaming pumps were put in place without further incident. I stood encased as in armor.

"What's this thing?" she asked from behind me. I executed a careful 180-degree turn.

"Oh, that's my cummerbund."

Her face lit up like an Italian sunrise. "A cummerbund!" She had seen Fred Astaire in many a cummerbund while he spun down marble staircases with Ginger Rogers in his arms, but it was the first actual specimen

332

she had ever been close to. She picked it up reverently, its paisley brilliance lighting up the room like an iridescent jewel.

"How does it work?" she asked, examining it closely. Before I could answer, she said, "Oh, I see. It has clips on the back. Hold still."

Around my waist it went. She drew it tight. The snaps clicked into place. It rode snugly halfway up my chest.

She picked up the snowy coat and held it out. I lowered my arms into it and straightened up. She darted around to the front, closed the single button and there I stood—Adonis!

Posing before the full-length mirror on the bathroom door, I noted the rich accent of my velvet stripes, the gleam of my pumps, the magnificent dash and sparkle of my high-fashion cummerbund. What a sight! What a feeling! This is the way life should be. This is what it's all about.

I heard my mother call out from the next room: "Hey, what's this thing?" She came out holding a cellophane bag containing a maroon object.

"Oh, that's my boutonniere."

"Your what?"

"It's a thing for the lapel. Like a fake flower."

It was the work of an instant to install my elegant wool carnation. It was the crowning touch. I was so overwhelmed that I didn't care about the fact that it didn't match my black tie, as Al had promised. With the cummerbund I was wearing, no one would notice, anyway.

333

Taking my leave as Cary Grant would have done, I sauntered out the front door, turned to give my mother a jaunty wave—just in time for her to call me back to pick up Wanda's corsage, which I'd left on the front-hall table.

Slipping carefully into the front seat with the cellophane-topped box safely beside me, I leaned forward slightly, to avoid wrinkling the back of my coat, started the motor up and shoved off into the warm summer night. A soft June moon hung overhead. The Ford purred like a kitten. When I pulled up before Wanda's house, it was lit up from top to bottom. Even before my brakes had stopped squealing, she was out on the porch, her mother fluttering about her, her father lurking in the background, beaming.

With stately tread, I moved up the walk; my pants were so tight that if I'd taken one false step, God knows what would have happened. In my sweaty, Aqua Velva-scented palm, I clutched the ritual largess in its shiny box.

Wanda wore a long turquoise taffeta gown, her milky skin and golden hair radiating in the glow of the porch light. This was *not* the old Wanda. For one thing, she didn't have her glasses on, and her eyes were unnaturally large and liquid, the way the true myopia victim's always are.

"Gee, thanks for the orchid," she whispered. Her voice sounded strained. In accordance with the tribal custom, she, too, was being mercilessly clamped by straps and girdles.

334

Her mother, an almost exact copy of Wanda, only slightly puffy here and there, said, "You'll take care of her now, won't you?"

"Now, Emily, don't start yapping," her old man muttered in the darkness. "They're not kids anymore."

They stood in the door as we drove off through the soft night toward Schwartz' house, our conversation stilted, our excitement almost at the boiling point. Schwartz rushed out of his house, his white coat like a ghost in the blackness, his hair agloam with Brylcreem, and surrounded by a palpable aura of Lifebuoy.

Five minutes later, Clara Mae piled into the back seat beside him, carefully holding up her daffodil-yellow skirts, her long slender neck arched. She, too, wasn't wearing her glasses. I had never realized that a good speller could be so pretty. Schwartz, a good half head shorter, laughed nervously as we tooled on toward the Cherry-wood Country Club. From all over town, other cars, polished and waxed, carried the rest of the junior class to their great trial by fire.

The club nestled amid the rolling hills, where the Sinclair oil aroma was only barely detectable. Parking the car in the lot, we threaded our way through the starched and crinolined crowd—the girls' girdles creaking in unison—to the grand ballroom. Japanese lanterns danced in the breeze through the open doors to the garden, bathing the dance floor in a fairytale glow.

I found myself saying things like, "Why, hello there, Albert, how are you?" And, "Yes, I believe the weather is perfect." Only Flick, the unregenerate Philistine, failed

335

to rise to the occasion. Already rumpled in his summer formal, he made a few tasteless wisecracks as Mickey Eisley and his Magic Music Makers struck up the sultry sounds that had made them famous in every steel-mill town that ringed Lake Michigan. Dark and sensuous, the dance floor engulfed us all. I felt tall, slim and beautiful, not realizing at the time that everybody feels that way wearing a white coat and rented pants. I could see myself standing on a mysterious balcony, a lonely, elegant figure, looking out over the lights of some exotic city, a scene of sophisticated gaiety behind me.

There was a hushed moment when Mickey Eisley stood in the baby spot, his wavy hair shining, before a microphone shaped like a chromium bullet.

"All right, boys and girls." The metallic ring of feedback framed his words in an echoing nimbus. "And now something really romantic. A request: *When the Swallows Come Back to Capistrano*. We're going to turn the lights down for this one."

Oh, wow! The lights faded even lower. Only the Japanese lanterns glowed dimly—red, green, yellow and blue —in the enchanted darkness. It was unquestionably the high point of my existence.

Wanda and I began to maneuver around the floor. My sole experience in dancing had been gained from reading Arthur Murray ads and practicing with a pillow for a partner behind the locked door of the bathroom. As we shuffled across the floor, I could see the black footprints before my eyes, marching on a white page: 1-2-3; then the white one that said, "Pause."

Back and forth, up and down, we moved metronomically. My box step was so square that I went in little right angles for weeks afterward. The wool carnation rode high up on my lapel and was beginning to scratch my cheek, and an insistent itch began to nag at my right shoulder. There was some kind of wire or horsehair or something in the shoulder pad that was beginning to bore its way into my flesh.

By now, my dashing concrete collar, far from having wilted, had set into the consistency of carborundum, and its incessant abrasive action had removed a wide strip of skin encircling my neck. As for my voice—due to the manic strangulation of the collar, it was now little more than a hoarse croak.

"When the swallows . . . retuuurrrrn to Capistraaaa-aaaano . . ." mooed the drummer, who doubled as the band's romantic vocalist.

I began to notice Wanda's orchid leering up at me from her shoulder. It was the most repulsive flower I had ever seen. At least 14 inches across, it looked like some kind of overgrown Venus's-flytrap waiting for the right moment to strike. Deep purple, with an obscene yellow tongue that stuck straight out of it, and greenish knobs on the end, it clashed almost audibly with her turquoise dress. It looked like it was breathing, and it clung to her shoulder as if with claws.

As I glided back and forth in my graceful box step, my left shoulder began to develop an itch that helped take my mind off of the insane itch in my right shoulder, which was beginning to feel like an army of hungry soldier ants on the march. The contortions I made to relieve the agony were camouflaged nicely by a short sneezing fit brought on by the orchid, which was exhaling directly into my face. So was Wanda, with a heady essence of Smith Brothers cough drops and sauerkraut.

"When the deeeep purpullllll fallllllls . . . Over sleeeeepy gaaardennnn walllls . . ." warbled the vocalist into his microphone, with which he seemed to be dancing the tango. The loudspeakers rattled in three-quarter time as Wanda started to sweat through her taffeta. I felt it running down her back. My own back was already so wet you could read the label on my undershirt right through the dinner jacket.

Back and forth we trudged doggedly across the crowded floor. Another Arthur Murray ad man, Schwartz was doing exactly the same step with Clara Mae directly behind me. We were all in a four-part lock step. As I hit the lower left-hand footprint in my square—the one marked "Pause"—he was hitting the upper right-hand corner of his square. Each time we did that, our elbows dug smartly into each other's ribs.

The jungle fragrance of the orchid was getting riper by the minute and the sweat, which had now saturated my jockey shorts, was pouring down my legs in rivulets. My soaked cummerbund turned two shades darker. So that she shouldn't notice, I pulled Wanda closer to me. Sighing, she hugged me back. Wanda was the vaguely chubby type of girl that was so popular at the time. Like Judy Garland, by whom she was heavily influenced, she strongly resembled a pink beach ball—but a *cute* beach ball, soft and rubbery. I felt bumpy things under her taffeta gown, with little hooks and knobs. Schwartz caught me a nasty shot in the rib cage just as I bent over to kiss her lightly on the bridge of her nose. It tasted salty. She looked up at me, her great liquid myopic eyes catching the reflection of the red and green lanterns overhead.

During a brief intermission, Schwartz and I carried paper cups dripping syrupy punch back to the girls, who had just spent some time in the ladies' room struggling unsuccessfully to repair the damage of the first half. As we were sipping, a face from my dim past floated by from out of nowhere—haughty, alabaster, green-eyed, dangerous.

"Hi, Daph," I muttered, spilling a little punch on my gleaming pumps, which had turned during the past hour into a pair of iron maidens.

"Oh, Howard." She spoke in the breathy, sexy way that such girls always have at proms. "I'd like you to meet Budge. Budge Cameron. He's at Princeton." A languid figure, probably born in a summer formal, loomed overhead.

"Budge, this is Howard."

"Hiya, fella." It was the first time I had heard the tight, nasal, swinging-jaw accent of the true Princetonian. It was not to be the last.

They were gone. Funny, I couldn't even remember actually dating her, I reflected, as the lights dimmed once again. We swung back into action. They opened with *Sleepy Lagoon*. 1-2-3-pause . . . 1-2-3-pause.

It was certain now. I had broken out in a raging rash.

I felt it spreading like lava across my shoulder blades under the sweat. The horsehair, meanwhile, had penetrated my chest cavity and was working its way toward a vital organ. Trying manfully to ignore it, I stared fixedly at the tiny turquoise ribbon that held Wanda's golden ponytail in place. With troubles of her own, she looked with an equally level gaze at my maroon-wool carnation, which by this time had wilted into a clump of lint.

All of a sudden, it was all over. The band played *Good Night, Sweetheart* and we were out—into a driving rain. A violent cloudburst had begun just as we reached the door. My poor little car, the pride and joy of my life, was outside in the lot. With the top down.

None of us, of course, had an umbrella. We stood under the canopy as the roaring thunderstorm raged on. It wasn't going to stop.

"You guys stay here. I'll get the car," I said finally. After all, I was in charge.

Plunging into the downpour, I sloshed through the puddles and finally reached the Ford. She must have had at least a foot of water in her already. Hair streaming down over my eyes, soaked to the skin and muddied to the knees. I bailed it out with a coffee can from the trunk, slid behind the wheel and pressed the automatic-top lever. Smooth as silk, it began to lift—and stuck halfway up. As the rain poured down in sheets and the lightning flashed, I pounded on the relays, furiously switched the lever off and on. I could see the country club dimly through the downpour. Finally, the top

340

groaned and flapped into place. I threw down the snaps, rolled up the windows and turned on the ignition; the battery was dead. The strain of hoisting that goddamn top had drained it dry. I yelled out the window at a passing car. It was Flick in his Chevy.

"GIMME A PUSH! MY BATTERY'S DEAD!"

This had never, to my knowledge, happened to Fred Astaire. And if it rained on Gene Kelly, he just sang.

Flick expertly swung his Chevy around and slammed into my trunk as I eased her into gear, and when she started to roll, the Ford shuddered and caught. Flick backed up and was gone, hollering out the window:

"SEE YOU AT THE ROOSTER."

Wanda, Schwartz and Clara Mae piled in on the damp, soggy seats and we took off. Do you know what happens to a maroon-wool carnation on a white-serge lapel in a heavy June downpour in the Midwest, where it rains not water but carbolic acid from the steel-mill fallout? I had a dark, wide, spreading maroon stripe that went all the way down to the bottom of my white coat. My French cuffs were covered with grease from fighting the top, and I had cracked a thumbnail, which was beginning to throb.

Undaunted, we slogged intrepidly through the rain toward the Red Rooster. Wedged against my side, Wanda looked up at me—oblivious to the elements—with luminous love eyes. She was truly an incurable romantic. Schwartz wisecracked in the back seat and Clara giggled from time to time. The savage tribal rite was nearing its final and most vicious phase.

341

We arrived at the Red Rooster, already crowded with other candidates for adulthood. A giant red neon rooster with a blue neon tail that flicked up and down in the rain set the tone for this glamorous establishment. An aura of undefined sin was always connected with the name Red Rooster. Sly winks, nudgings and adolescent cacklings about what purportedly went on at the Rooster made it the "in" spot for such a momentous revel. Its waiters were rumored really to be secret henchmen of the Mafia. But the only thing we knew for sure about the Rooster was that anybody on the far side of seven years old could procure any known drink without question.

The decor ran heavily to red-checkered-oilcloth table covers and plastic violets, and the musical background was provided by a legendary jukebox that stood a full seven feet high, featuring red and blue cascading waterfalls that gushed endlessly though its voluptuous façade. In full 200-watt operation, it could be *felt*, if not clearly heard, as far north as Gary and as far south as Kankakee. A triumph of American aesthetics.

Surging with anticipation, I guided Wanda through the uproarious throng of my peers. Schwartz and Clara Mae trailed behind, exchanging ribald remarks with the gang.

We occupied the only remaining table. Immediately, a beady-eyed waiter, hair glistening with Vaseline Hair Oil, sidled over and hovered like a vulture. Quickly distributing the famous Red Rooster Ala Carte Deluxe Menu, he stood back, smirking, and waited for us to impress our dates.

"Can I bring you anything to drink, gentlemen?" he said, heavily accenting the gentlemen.

My first impulse was to order my favorite drink of the period, a bottled chocolate concoction called Kayo, the Wonder Drink; but remembering that better things were expected of me on prom night, I said, in my deepest voice, "Uh . . . make mine . . . bourbon."

Schwartz grunted in admiration. Wanda ogled me with great, swimming, lovesick eyes. Bourbon was the only drink that I had actually heard of. My old man ordered it often down at the Bluebird Tavern. I had always wondered what it tasted like. I was soon to find out.

"How will you have it, sir?"

"Well, in a glass, I guess." I had failed to grasp the subtlety of his question, but the waiter snorted in appreciation of my humorous sally.

"Rocks?" he continued.

Rocks? I had heard about getting your rocks, but never in a restaurant. Oh, well, what the hell.

"Sure," I said. "Why not?"

All around me, the merrymaking throng was swinging into high gear. Carried away by it all, I added a phrase I had heard my old man use often: "And make it a triple." I had some vague idea that this was a brand or something.

"A *triple*? Yes, sir." His eyes snapped wide—in respect, I gathered. He knew he was in the presence of a serious drinker.

The waiter turned his gaze in Schwartz' direction. "And you, sir?"

"Make it the same." Schwartz had never been a leader. The die was cast. Pink ladies, at the waiter's suggestion, were ordered for the girls, and we then proceeded to scan the immense menu with feigned disinterest. When the waiter returned with our drinks, I ordered—for reasons that even today I am unable to explain—lamb chops, yellow turnips, mashed potatoes and gravy, a side dish of the famous Red Rooster Roquefort Italian Cole Slaw— and a strawberry shortcake. The others wisely decided to stick with their drinks.

Munching bread sticks, Wanda, Schwartz, Clara and I engaged in sophisticated postprom repartee. Moment by moment, I felt my strength and maturity, my dashing bonhomie, my clean-cut handsomeness enveloping my friends in its benevolent warmth. Schwartz, too, seemed to scintillate as never before. Clara giggled and Wanda sighed, overcome by the romance of it all. Even when Flick, sitting three tables away, clipped Schwartz behind the left ear with a poppyseed roll, our urbanity remained unruffled.

Before me reposed a sparkling tumbler of beautiful amber liquid, ice cubes bobbing merrily on its surface, a plastic swizzle stick sporting an enormous red rooster sticking out at a jaunty angle. Schwartz was similarly equipped. And the fluffy pink ladies looked lovely in the reflected light of the pulsating jukebox.

I had seen my old man deal with just this sort of situation. Raising my beaded glass, I looked around at my companions and said suavely, "Well, here's mud in yer eye." Clara giggled; Wanda sighed dreamily, now

344

totally in love with this man of the world who sat across from her on this, our finest night.

"Yep," Schwartz parried wittily, hoisting his glass high and slopping a little bourbon on his pants as he did so.

Swiftly, I brought the bourbon to my lips, intending to down it in a single devil-may-care draught, the way Gary Cooper used to do in the Silver Dollar Saloon. I did, and Schwartz followed suit. Down it went—a screaming 90-proof rocket searing savagely down my gullet. For an instant, I sat stunned, unable to comprehend what had happened. Eyes watering copiously, I had a brief urge to sneeze, but my throat seemed to be paralyzed. Wanda and Clara Mae swam before my misted vision; and Schwartz seemed to have disappeared under the table. He popped up again—face beet-red, eyes bugging, jaw slack, tongue lolling.

"Isn't this romantic? Isn't this the most wonderful night in all our lives? I will forever treasure the memories of this wonderful night." From far off, echoing as from some subterranean tunnel, I heard Wanda speaking.

Deep down in the pit of my stomach, I felt crackling flames licking at my innards. I struggled to reply, to maintain my élan, my fabled *savoir-faire*. "Urk . . . urk . . . . yeah," I finally managed with superhuman effort.

Wanda swam hazily into focus. She was gazing across the table at me with adoring eyes.

"Another, gents?" The waiter was back, still smirking.

Schwartz nodded dumbly. I just sat there, afraid to move. An instant later, two more triple bourbons materialized in front of us.

Clara raised her pink lady high and said reverently, "Let's drink to the happiest night of our lives."

There was no turning back. Another screamer rocketed down the hatch. For an instant, it seemed as though this one wasn't going to be as lethal as the first, but the room suddenly tilted sideways. I felt torrents of cold sweat pouring from my forehead. Clinging to the edge of the table, I watched as Schwartz gagged across from me. Flick, I noticed, had just chugalugged his third rum and coke and was eating a cheeseburger with the works.

The conflagration deep inside me was now clearly out of control. My feet were smoking; my diaphragm heaved convulsively, jiggling my cummerbund; and Schwartz began to shrink, his face alternating between purple-red and chalk-white, his eyes black holes staring fixedly at the ketchup bottle. He sat stock-still. Wanda, meanwhile, cooed on ecstatically—but I was beyond understanding what she was saying. Faster and faster, in ever-widening circles, the room, the jukebox, the crowd swirled dizzily about me. In all the excitement of preparations for the prom, I realized that I hadn't eaten a single thing all day.

Out of the maelstrom, a plate mysteriously appeared before me; paper-pantied lamb chops hissing in bubbling grease, piled yellow turnips, gray mashed potatoes awash in rich brown gravy. Maybe this would help, I thought incoherently. Grasping my knife and fork as firmly as I could, I poised to whack off a piece of meat. Suddenly, the landscape listed 45 degrees to starboard and the

346

chop I was about to attack skidded off my plate—plowing a swath through the mashed potatoes—and right into the aisle.

Pretending not to notice, I addressed myself to the remaining chop, which slid around, eluding my grasp, until I managed to skewer it with my fork. Hacking off a chunk, I jammed it fiercely mouthward, missing my target completely. Still impaled on my fork, the chop slithered over my cheekbone, spraying gravy as it went, all over my white lapels. On the next try, I had better luck, and finally I managed to get the whole chop down.

To my surprise, I didn't feel any better. Maybe the turnips will help, I thought. Lowering my head to within an inch of the plate to prevent embarrassing mishaps, I shoveled them in—but the flames within only fanned higher and higher. I tried the potatoes and gravy. My legs began to turn cold. I wolfed down the Red Rooster Roquefort Italian Cole Slaw. My stomach began to rise like a helium balloon, bobbing slowly up the alimentary canal.

My nose low over the heaping dish of strawberry shortcake, piled high with whipped cream and running with juice, I knew at last for a dead certainty what I had to do before it happened right here in front of everybody. I struggled to my feet. A strange rubbery numbness had struck my extremities. I tottered from chair to chair, grasping for the wall. There was a buzzing in my ears.

Twenty seconds later, I was on my knees, gripping the bowl of the john like a life preserver in pitching

347

seas. Schwartz, imitating me as usual, lay almost prostrate on the tiles beside me, his body racked with heaving sobs. Lamb chops, bourbon, turnips, mashed potatoes, cole slaw—all of it came rushing out of me in a great roaring torrent—out of my mouth, my nose, my ears, my very soul. Then Schwartz opened up, and we took turns retching and shuddering. A head thrust itself between us directly into the pot. It was Flick moaning wretchedly. Up came the cheeseburger, the rum and Cokes, pretzels, potato chips, punch, gumdrops, a corned-beef sandwich, a fingernail or two—everything he'd eaten for the last week. For long minutes, the three of us lay there limp and quivering, smelling to high heaven, too weak to get up. It was the absolute high point of the junior prom; the rest was anticlimax.

Finally, we returned to the table, ashen-faced and shaking. Schwartz, his coat stained and rumpled, sat Zombie-like across from me. The girls didn't say much. Pink ladies just aren't straight bourbon.

But our little group played the scene out bravely to the end. My dinner jacket was now even more redolent and disreputable than when I'd first seen it on the hanger at Al's. And my bow tie, which had hung for a while by one clip, had somehow disappeared completely, perhaps flushed into eternity with all the rest. But as time wore on, my hearing and eyesight began slowly to return; my legs began to lose their rubberiness and the room slowly resumed its even keel—at least even enough to consider getting up and leaving. The waiter seemed to know. He returned as if on cue, bearing a slip of paper.

"The damages, gentlemen."

Taking the old man's $20 out of my wallet, I handed it to him with as much of a flourish as I could muster. There wouldn't have been any point in looking over the check; I wouldn't have been able to read it, anyway. In one last attempt to recoup my cosmopolitan image, I said offhandedly, "Keep the change." Wanda beamed in unconcealed ecstasy.

The drive home in the damp car was not quite the same as the one that had begun the evening so many weeks earlier. Our rapidly fermenting coats made the enclosed air rich and gamy, and Schwartz, who had stopped belching, sat with head pulled low between his shoulder blades, staring straight ahead. Only the girls preserved the joyousness of the occasion. Women always survive.

In a daze, I dropped off Schwartz and Clara Mae and drove in silence toward Wanda's home, the faint light of dawn beginning to show in the east.

We stood on her porch for the last ritual encounter. A chill dawn wind rustled the lilac bushes.

"This was the most wonderful, wonderful night of my whole life. I always dreamed the prom would be like this," breathed Wanda, gazing passionately up into my watering eyes.

"Me, too," was all I could manage.

I knew what was expected of me now. Her eyes closed dreamily. Swaying slightly, I leaned forward—and the faint odor of sauerkraut from her parted lips coiled slowly up to my nostrils. This was not in the script. I knew I had better get off that porch fast, or else. Backpedaling

349

desperately and down the stairs, I blurted, "Bye!" and—fighting down my rising gorge—clamped my mouth tight, leaped into the Ford, burned rubber and tore off into the dawn. Two blocks away, I squealed to a stop alongside a vacant lot containing only a huge Sherwin-Williams paint sign. WE COVER THE WORLD, it aptly read. In the blessed darkness behind the sign, concealed from prying eyes, I completed the final rite of the ceremony.

The sun was just rising as I swung the car up the driveway and eased myself quietly into the kitchen. The old man, who was going fishing that morning, sat at the enamel table sipping black coffee. He looked up as I came in. I was in no mood for idle chatter.

"You look like you had a hell of a prom," was all he said.

"I sure did."

The yellow kitchen light glared harshly on my muddy pants, my maroon-streaked, vomit-stained white coat, my cracked fingernail, my greasy shirt.

"You want anything to eat?" he asked sardonically.

At the word "eat," my stomach heaved convulsively. I shook my head numbly.

"That's what I thought," he said. "Get some sleep. You'll feel better in a couple of days, when your head stops banging."

He went back to reading his paper. I staggered into my bedroom, dropping bits of clothing as I went. My soggy Hollywood paisley cummerbund, the veteran of another gala night, was flung beneath my dresser as I toppled into bed. My brother muttered in his sleep across the room. He was still a kid. But his time would come.

350